ADDICTIVE AWARENESS

Thomas Byrd

Health Sciences,
De Anza College, Cupertino, CA

KENDALL/HUNT PUBLISHING COMPANY
2460 Kerper Boulevard   P.O. Box 539   Dubuque, Iowa 52004-0539

To the Community of Goose Creek, South Carolina

Cover design   Mark van Bronkhorst
Photography   Patrick Byrd
Model   Marika Pesola

CONTENTS

required dealers and dispensers of opiates and cocaine to register and to pay an annual fee. It also stipulated that patients could purchase or possess narcotics if they are prescribed by a physician in the course of professional practice for legitimate medical purposes. The pharmacological revolution accelerated with the development of vaccines. The Federal Government enacted the Controlled Substances Act of 1970 which established five categories of drugs listing potentially abused medications. The harshest penalties are for Schedule I and II.

Schedule I:

The drugs listed in schedule I have the highest potential for abuse and dependence. There is usually no recognized medical use in the United States outside of specific research institutions. Obtaining a drug of this type involves extensive paperwork.

Schedule II

Such drugs have a currently acceptable medical use in the United States, but have a high potential for abuse. Most narcotics are listed in Schedule II, along with all amphetamine—type compounds and most barbiturates. Extensive paperwork is also required when these drugs are shipped. Prescriptions may be telephoned to a pharmacy only in an emergency and the physician is required to provide the pharmacy with a written prescription within 72 hours.

Schedule III

These are substances with a potential for abuse less than Schedule I and II. These drugs have a moderate potential for abuse. Drugs in this category are viewed by the government as having the potential of leading to varying degrees of physical reliance, or high psychological dependence. Prescriptions can be telephoned to a pharmacy by a physician, and can be refilled up to five times within six months, if the original prescription permits it.

Schedule IV

These are substances with a low potential for abuse relative to drugs in Schedule III. These drugs have a currently accepted medical use in the United States. They include some sedatives and some non narcotic analgesics. Physical or psychological dependence is limited. Prescription requirements are the same as Schedule III requirements.

Schedule V

These drugs are predominately mixtures containing small amount of narcotics and are used as an antidiarrheal or antitussive medication. In other

Schedule I

Stimulants:
Amphetamine
variants:
MDMA

Narcotic Analgesics:
Heroin

Hallucinogens:
Analogs of Phencyclidine:
PCE, TCP, PHP
Mescaline, Peyote
Marijuana
Psilocybin

Sedative Depressants:
Methadone
Methaqualone

Schedule II

Stimulants:
Cocaine
Methamphetamine
Methylphenidate(Ritalin)
Amphetamines

Narcotic Analgesics:
Opium
Morphine
Codeine
Hydromorphone(Dilaudid)
Meperidine (Demerol)
Oxycodone (Percodan)
Fentanyl

Sedative Depressants:
Amobarbital
Pentobarbital
Secobarbital

Schedule III

Stimulants:
Benzphatamine Hydrochloride
(Didrex)
Mazindol (Mazandor)
Phendimetrazine Tartrate
(all three are anoretic agents)

Sedatives/Narcotics
Deriatives of barbituric acid except
those listed in another schedule.
Glutethimide (Doriden)
Methyprylon (Nodular)

Narcotic Analegics:
APC + Codeine
Acetaminophen + Codeine
Nalorphine

Schedule IV

Sedatives and Depressants
Barital
Phenobarbital
Chloral hydrate
Ethchlorvynol (Placicyl)
Ethinamate (Valmid)
Propoxyphene (Darvon)
Pentazocine (Talwin)

Benzodiazepines:
Alprazolam (Xanax)
Ativan
Buspar
Centrax
Diazepam (Valium)
Librium
Meprobamate (Miltown)
Restoril
Serax
Tranxene
Triazolam (Halcion)

Schedule V

Preparations containing limited quantities of narcotic drugs used generally for antitussive and antidiarrheal purposes.

Lomotil
Actifed with codeine cough syrup
Triminic expectorant with codeine.

words, to control diarrhea and coughs. Any mixture may lead to limited physical or psychological dependence. (Availability without prescription depends upon individual state laws).

How a Drug is Tested

Phase 1 trial

First tests of a new drug in humans, specifically aims to measure the drug's side effects. Typically, about 20 people are given the drug in a range of doses, starting with a very low dose and gradually increasing to a dose much higher than doctors would use in treatment. No one is given a placebo. Every symptom, even a common headache, is charted and reported to the drug company. Duration: Three to eight months.

Phase 2 trial

An attempt to measure the drug's effectiveness. Typically, 100 to 200 volunteers are given each dose used in the tests, and half unknowingly receive either a placebo or another drug that is a standard treatment. Duration: At least eight months but the tests can take up to two years.

Phase 3 trial

Broader, longer tests that can be skipped if the drug shows effectiveness earlier and is needed to treat fatal illnesses. Typically, 300 to 3,000 people are given the drug in this last phase; half may receive a placebo or another drug for comparison. Duration: One to four years.

Treatment investigational new drug (IND) status

Once a drug has passed all three phases of tests, the FDA will sometimes allow it to be given to physicians and used in treatment pending final marketing approval. In the case of AIDS drugs and others used in fatal illnesses, the FDA sometimes will grant IND status immediately after Phase 2 trials. [3]

Effects of Drugs in the Body

The values or hazards of any new drug are determined through tests in which one drug alone is used. It is unrealistic to assume that a drug will produce the same effect when used with another drug. One drug may markedly influence the action of another.

There are many possible actions of drugs. One of the actions is to increase the production of compounds that can act on other substances that can change the drugs to which the body is exposed. The increase of liver enzymes that can reduce the action of drugs has been observed to occur when people are exposed to a variety of drugs, pesticides, food additives, and hydrocarbons in the environment. When the drug is broken down it may be advantageous to the body. In this case, the increase in the production of liver enzymes may lessen the effect of the drug. On the other hand, the products of drug breakdown or metabolism are sometimes equal to or greater than the toxicity of the parent drug. Certain drugs can inhibit the metabolism of other drugs. Some drugs can intensify the actions of others.

It is essential that the nature and importance of multiple reactions be better understood. Some persons metabolize a drug so rapidly that effective blood and tissue levels are not achieved, whereas other persons metabolize the same drug so slowly that toxic effects occur. The measurement of blood levels of any drug used by the physician is a necessity.

It is difficult to predict how a particular person may react to a drug. Individual differences in rates of metabolism can vary tremendously. For example, the biologic half-life of one anticoagulant drug may vary tenfold. The half-life of valium may be extended to 3–5 days if a woman is taking birth control pills.

How Drugs Affect the Brain

Investigators rely mainly on electrophysiology, which is concerned with the electrical properties of tissues, to study how drugs exert their influence. When nerve cells are active, they produce minute electrical potentials. In the brain these electrical potentials appear as waves which can be recorded on a moving strip of paper, the electroencephalogram. These waves change with different states of the central nervous system.

The control of sleep and wakefulness is exerted by a structure known as the reticular formation of the brain stem. This structure also controls respiration, blood pressure, and spinal reflexes. Changes in the level of activity in the reticular formation may occur in response to influences such as hormones, blood pressure, and drugs, as well as to other sensory information.

Two groups of drugs, the depressants and the stimulants, have opposite effects. The barbiturates produce depressant effects by a direct action on mechanisms located in the reticular formation which are concerned with wakefulness. These drugs block the conduction of nerve impulses, and sleep. Loss of consciousness may ensue. The stimulants (i.e.cocaine, methamphetamine), on the other hand, increase the activity of the nerve cells, and thereby increase wakefulness and alertness.

Drugs such as tranquilizers have more subtle effects on the brain. They reduce sensory influences, and so prevent the patient from being agitated by events around them.

6

Experiments with hallucinogenic drugs like LSD-25 show that sensory stimuli are facilitated rather than impeded. The actions of both LSD-25 and tranquilizers are closely linked to the filtering and integrating of sensory information by the brain. Many of the symptoms which LSD-25 produce closely resemble schizophrenia.

Drugs During Pregnancy

Large numbers of pregnant women receive prenatal vitamins with iron. Fortunately, the number of prescription drugs used during the first three months of pregnancy (especially those used to control nausea and vomiting) in this country during the past 10 years have been sharply reduced. The wise physician will markedly restrict the drugs prescribed for patients during all stages of pregnancy. Over-the-counter products should receive the approval of the physician before the patient makes a purchase. Good pre-natal care will greatly reduce the risk of unnecessary problems. Soda crackers and bananas are frequently recommended to help curb the nausea experienced in early pregnancy.

Birth defects can result from some abnormality within the individual or from some external stimulus. In malformations that are genetic in origin the basis for the defect is in the sperm, the egg, or both. On the other hand, the genetic inheritance may be normal, but the embryo may be affected by drugs, or by other factors. If normal development is interfered with, a defect will result.

Since the mother will house the fetus for approximately 40 weeks, the health of these individuals is of utmost importance. Prenatal care should focus on educating the woman in optimum health pursuits and psychological preparation for the birth. Good prenatal care reduces the rate of prematurity significantly. Many external factors during pregnancy are to be strongly condemned (examples: the use of drugs, tobacco, alcohol, X-rays, and so on). The problems are complex.

Some drugs during pregnancy may cause gross abnormalities or other disturbances in the baby. Often, whether or not a drug will injure the unborn baby will depend on the time during pregnancy that the drug is taken. *The earlier the drug is taken, the greater the damage. The first trimester is the most critical. The best child care begins during pregnancy.* Enzyme systems of many body organs, and possibly the placenta, play an important role in making drugs harmless. If there is interference with these enzyme systems, so that the drugs cannot be detoxified, then damage may be done.

Every type of substance passes from the maternal blood to the fetal blood during pregnancy. Most of the drugs that women take during pregnancy appear to be transferred across the placenta by simple diffusion. Drugs that are soluble in lipid (fat like substances) and contain non-ionized molecules appear to pass the placental barrier most rapidly.

7

Drugs produce damaging effects on the unborn baby at different times for different organs or systems. Thus the nervous system is most apt to be damaged by drugs during the 15th to 25th day of pregnancy; the eye is most apt to be damaged during the 24th to 30th day, the legs from the 24th to 36th day, and the heart from the 20th to the 40th day. Some drugs may have no significant effect upon the unborn baby. Others may cause abortion or death; others may affect the body structure of the baby; still others can be expected to cause metabolic, biochemical, and other changes that are injurious.

The duration and intensity of many drugs depend on the action of enzymes located in the liver. The fetus and newborn infant are more sensitive than the adult to many drugs. The physician must exert great care in giving drugs to infants or to an expectant mother. Barbiturates, narcotics and other drugs pass across the placental barrier and may cause a deficiency of oxygen in the unborn child. An explanation for this sensitivity to drugs lies in the fact that newborns do not yet have certain fully developed enzyme systems for the metabolism of many drugs.

It must be noted that kidney function in the newborn infant is only 30 to 40 percent as efficient as that of the adult. Most drugs have to undergo metabolic changes before they are readily available for excretion by the kidney.

Fat content may be 16 times greater in the full term infant than the premature infant. These differences in body composition can be expected to be related to the distribution of drugs throughout the body.

Fetal Alcohol Syndrome and Fetal Alcohol Effects

Women are now heavily targeted for marketing of alcoholic beverages. According to Impact, a liquor industry newsletter, women will spend $30 billion on alcoholic beverages in 1994, compared to $20 billion in 1984.

Fetal alcohol syndrome is an entirely preventable problem. For a woman who never drinks during her pregnancy, there is a zero percentage chance of her baby having this problem. The abuse of alcohol during pregnancy appears to be the most frequent cause of mental defectiveness throughout the entire Western world. Fetal Alcohol Syndrome (FAS) is among the leading known causes of birth defects with accompanying mental retardation.

The amount of alcohol that can be safely consumed has not been established. Getting the truth from an alcoholic woman who has delivered a defective child is difficult at best. She doesn't have the answers in most cases. Autopsy studies of aborted FAS babies can document the exact time of the binge drinking due to growth abnormalities in the brain. However, we have our own individual susceptibilities. Fetal Alcohol Effects (FAE) are those signs in the offspring that have been linked to alcohol use during pregnancy by the mother which do not meet the diagnostic criteria for full-blown Fetal Alcohol Syndrome.

There is no established safe dose of alcohol during pregnancy, nor does there seem to be a safe time to drink. Just as startling, recent evidence from animal and human subjects suggest that infants fathered by heavy drinking males may also have an increased risk of birth defects. Women who breast-feed should continue to abstain from drinking alcohol until their babies are weaned, because alcohol readily enters breast milk and is transmitted to the nursing infant. One in six women in the peak childbearing years of 18–34 may drink enough, either chronically or episodically, to present a hazard to an unborn infant.

―――――――――――――――― QUOTATION ――――――――――――――――
"When you take cocaine, it feels as if it's the most important function in life, because cocaine causes your body and brain to send those life-orienting and life-producing signals: the need for sex, food, water, flight. So of course you take more. Cocaine in the disease state becomes pre-eminent over survival of the individual".

Dr. Mark Gold, Director of Research
at Fair Oaks Hospital in Summit, New Jersey,
who established the National Cocaine Hotline.

Cocaine During Pregnancy

The increasing abuse of cocaine by women causes parallel concern about the use of the drug during pregnancy. Women who abuse cocaine may have ir-regular menstrual cycles or none at all and still be able to become pregnant. There has been an increasing association of pregnancy complications and the use of cocaine including premature detachment of the placenta. In addition, because of cocaine's appetite-suppressing effects, some women may attempt to keep their weight down during pregnancy, compromising their nutritional needs and interfering with the pregnancy. It has also been found that cocaine passes into breast milk.

Four medical scientists of the Memorial Hospital and the Northwestern Medical School in Chicago conducted research on the infants of 23 cocaine-using women who were divided into two groups, one of which was using only cocaine while the other half was using cocaine and some other drugs. These women were compared with others who were not using drugs at all.

The scientists believe the findings indicate that cocaine is indeed harm-ful to the unborn baby. Members of the research team observe that much evidence is already available to verify the damaging effects of many drugs on the unborn child. These "cocaine babies" can begin life in an "agoniz-ing state of withdrawal" that can last up to two to three weeks, can have higher-than-normal rates of respiratory and kidney troubles, often have visual problems and show a lack of coordination and developmental retardation. Additionally, there is a 38 percent chance of miscarriage in pregnant women who use cocaine, and because of cocaine-induced fluctuations in blood pressure there can be prenatal strokes in the fragile vessels, rendering the child potentially paralyzed at birth.

1. The cocaine using women had a higher rate of spontaneous abortion.
2. The cocaine babies exhibited more trembling and had greater startle responses than those infants whose mothers had not used the drug during pregnancy.
3. Constriction of blood vessels in cocaine-using mothers caused a reduction in normal blood flow to the unborn baby.
4. By the age of 2 weeks, one cocaine baby died.
5. A second baby died later.
6. A deformed baby was born to a woman who used 4 to 5 grams in a single day, then stopped until the last one-third of her pregnancy.

The scientists also urge that special attention be given to the presence of abnormal physical activity and extended crying on the part of the newborn as an indication of narcotic addiction. Cocaine may be used in conjunction with heroin.

Anabolic Steroids

Steroids are synthetic male hormones that are increasingly being abused for cosmetic and athletic reasons. These hormones can be obtained both from legal and black market dealers. Steroids are taken in various cycles of pills or injectables. Used in conjunction with training, the drugs stimulate cellular processes that build body muscle.

The drug-enhanced physique is a hazardous bargain. Steroids can cause temporary acne and balding, upset hormonal production and damage to the heart and kidneys. Physicians suspect they may contribute to liver cancers and atherosclerosis. Among teens, who are already undergoing physical and psychological stresses, there can be some enhanced risks. The drugs can stunt growth by accelerating bone maturation. Doctors also speculate the chemicals may compromise still developing reproductive systems. Steroid users have reported a shrinking of testicles and impotence.

There is also a worrisome threat to mental health. Drug users are prone to moodiness, depression, irritability and rage.

When you put big egos and big dreams together with steroids, that's a nasty combination. Quitting steroids is difficult. Muscles fade rapidly. A self-image that relies on a steroid-drenched body may be difficult to change.

Angel Dust

Phencyclidine was experimentally used as an anesthetic agent in surgery during the 1950's, but was abandoned because of patient agitation and delirium that lasted for hours.

On the street, the drug is known under 20 or more names, including "Angel Dust," "PCP," "Blast," and "KJ". It appears in many forms and can often be mixed with parsley and smoked. Cigarettes may be dipped into a liquid, dried, and smoked. The drug, or an analog of Phencyclidine can be smoked, inhaled, eaten or injected.

This psychedelic drug has, in low dosage, comparable effects to many other substances of this nature, but is related to severe disturbances of mind and body as dosages are increased. Symptoms resembling schizophrenia may appear and last for days or longer.

Both physical and psychological reactions may be very severe. Chaotic mental activity, agitation, incoherence, catatonic posturing, stupor, aimless running, auditory and visual hallucinations, aggressive activity against others, unpredictable destructiveness, dangerous paranoid delusions of persecution or other behaviors have all been observed in persons under the influence of phencyclidine. If recovery from a toxic reaction to PCP occurs there may be complete loss of memory for the episode. Although it may be difficult for the doctor to distinguish between PCP psychosis and schizophrenia, it is important to do so because emergency treatments are quite different. The drugs for schizophrenia may cause a deadly speeding up of the heart as well as dangerous low blood pressure in patients with PCP psychosis.

All of these reactions do not occur every time PCP is used. In fact, some users may find PCP trips to be pleasant and may thus be encouraged to continue using the drug. However, the ultimate expectation of serious consequences makes this hallucinogenic drug a problem of major concern.

People who persist in using PCP after an adverse reaction will continue to have psychotic responses to the drug, and may well suffer from chronic anxiety, confusion, as well as other severe impairments of mental functioning.

Phencyclidine is a Schedule 1 drug, with little or no medical use and a high potential for abuse. It is made by street chemists and formulas vary. Analogs are common. It is fat soluble and flashbacks can occur up to months after the last dose. The effect is often dose related.

Low doses act as a central nervous system depressant; middle level doses act as a hallucinogen; high doses produce a psychotic episode; very high doses may cause death by respiratory depression. Some effects may include: 1) extreme muscular rigidity; 2) a "moon walk," caused by perceptual difficulties, causing an inability to walk steadily; 3) a 20–30 percent increase in blood pressure; 4) a rise in body temperature; 5) decreased sen-

11

sitivity or impervious to pain; 6) superhuman strength and; 7) both horizontal and vertical nystagmus (involuntary, rapid movements of the eyeball).

There are three basic rules concerning the treatment of a PCP overdose: 1) don't touch; 2) don't turn on the lights; 3) don't make any noise. In the hospital the patient is placed in a quiet, dimly lighted room and permitted to complete the experience. Fruit juices, food, and comfort are provided during the approximate three days it takes to come down.

Altered States of Consciousness

Arnold Ludwig M.D. published an article in the Archives of General Psychiatry reviewing 84 research articles on the subject of alteration of the mind through the use of LSD and considered his own experimental reactions to this drug. Psilocybin, Mescaline, MDMA, Phencyclidine or Cannibas all have the capability to produce one or more thought disorders in some degree.

1. Changes in thinking. Disturbances in concentration, attention, memory and judgment are common findings in an altered state of consciousness. Archaic modes of thought predominate and recognition of reality is impaired.

2. Disturbed time sense. The sense of time is greatly changed. Subjective feelings of time may come to a standstill, acceleration or slowing, and a sense of timelessness may occur.

3. Loss of control. There is often fear of losing the grip on reality and of losing self-control. Loss of conscious control may arouse feelings of impotency and helplessness, although the subject may gain a sense of greater control and power through self-identification with a supernatural power.

4. Changes in Emotional Expression. Sudden and unexpected displays of a more primitive and intense emotion often occur. Emotional extremes from ecstasy to fear and depression can be expected.

5. Separation of body and mind. Distortions in body image commonly occur. A profound sense of depersonalization may occur, in which there is a distinction between body and mind and a dissolution between self and others, the world, or the universe. Various parts of the body may seem to be shrunken, enlarged, distorted, heavy, or weightless.

6. Distortions of perceptions. Hallucinations, perceptual aberrations, increased visual imagery, and illusions of every variety may occur.

7. Changes in meaning or significance. Persons with an altered state of consciousness may attach increased meaning or significance to their experience, ideas, or projections. There may be what appears as a

12

profound experience involving insight and truth to the point of "psychotic insight," but the conviction may actually be ridiculous.

For an example of a distorted sense of significance, the physician reports that in his own experimental use of LSD he had an intense desire to urinate. Standing at the urinal he read the sign above it "Please Flush After Using!" As he weighed these words in his mind they seemed suddenly to have a profound meaning. He rushed back to a colleague to share this universal truth with him, but the latter could not appreciate the world-shaking significance of the communication.

8. A sense of inability to explain. Often, persons claim an inability to communicate the nature of their experience to anyone who has not undergone the same experience. Amnesia for parts of the experience may be a factor in inability to communicate.

9. Feelings of rejuvenation. On emerging from certain profound alterations of consciousness certain persons claim to experience a new sense of hope, rebirth, or rejuvenation.

10. Hypersuggestibility. There is a tendency to perceive or misinterpret various stimuli, according to inner fears or wishes. With recession of the capacity for expression of critical judgment there is a decrease in the capacity for the recognition of reality. Often, in an attempt to compensate for failing critical faculties, the person comes to rely more on the suggestions of others who represent some kind of authority. Suggestions from an "authority" tend to be accepted as concrete reality.

In some persons, a state of anxiety ranging from mild apprehension to panic occurs. The threatening situation arises out of an extremely complex drug scene involving multiple drugs, the user's mood or mind set, unknown compounds, adulterations, and contamination. An ever-increasing list of new drugs leads to drug fads as the popularity of one drug gives way to another. Illusions and hallucinations can be highly terrifying. Victims may feel that they are going to lose control and never come back. An important indicator of how severe the reaction depends on the degree to which a person can recognize that it is drug-induced and that the effects will pass. In defining reality it must be explained over and over that distortions and frightening feelings are due to the drug.

QUESTION

How Long Does Marijuana (Cannabinoids, THC) Remain in the Urine?

The detection period for marijuana depends a lot on the smoker's pattern of use. Several studies have shown that if the cutoff level of 100ng/ml (the threshold used by most workplace testing programs) is used, it is highly unlikely that a person would remain positive for more than three days after using moderate amounts of marijuana. If higher amounts are used, this detection period will be longer. If large amounts of the drug are used daily for more than a week, there is a very small possibility that the user could remain positive at the 100ng/ml cutoff level for as long as a month after discontinuing use. (See the August 1987 issue of the PharChem Newsletter for an in-depth discussion of marijuana and its detection in the urine.) [1]

Marijuana

The Council on Scientific Affairs of the American Medical Association observes that despite the fact that marijuana has some value in medical treatment there continues to be evidence that it is hazardous to health.

There is acceptable scientific evidence that marijuana can help prevent nausea and vomiting in people with cancer who are being treated by chemotherapy. The drug also helps reduce the intraocular pressure in some glaucoma patients, thus helping to preserve their vision. The active ingredient THC (tetrahydrocannabinol) is now manufactured by pharmaceutical companies in 2mg., 5mg., and 10 mg. tablets. Doctors can prescribe an appropriate dosage to a patient who is not responding to other types of treatment. Lung irritation will not occur.

The Council believes that drug abuse can have its most serious effects with "at risk" persons, such as children and adolescents. The research team identifies the following harmful effects from the use of marijuana.

1. Brain Capacity. Abundant studies show that the drug impairs the desire to learn, as well as the capacity to do so. Thinking power, memory, degree of attention and general productivity are all affected for the worse, as is social adjustment. Psychological preoccupation with the drug reduces still further the ability to meet the responsibilities of daily living. Chronic use in the formative years interferes with the normal handling of anxiety, dealing with stress, and other coping mechanisms leading to psychological maturity. The motivational syndrome may be a chemically induced deterrent making it difficult to stop smoking marijuana.

2. Respiration. Irritation of the lungs and bronchial tubes from the smoking of marijuana has been well proven by research. The vital capacity of the lungs has been reduced. Analysis of the chemical contents in marijuana as compared to tobacco clearly reveals there is more tar in "pot" and there are more carcinogenic substances in the tar of Cannibas smoke. Furthermore, the inhalation of smoke from a marijuana cigarette is much deeper and is kept in the lung for a long time.

3. Functioning of the Heart. Tachycardia (excessive rapid heart beat) is regularly seen, and heart patients have their capacities for exercise impaired.

4. Neurological capacities such as reaction time, physical coordination and visual perception are all impaired. Overall driving ability is further impaired by errors in concentration and perceptual difficulties. Driving a car or operating machinery of any kind becomes more dangerous.

5. Diminished Reproductive Abilities. There is a growing body of information that points to diminished fertility, endocrine changes, and threats to the unborn. Long term use of marijuana may cause abnormal menstruation and failure to ovulate besides injury to a fetus in a pregnancy. According to some studies, infant mortality rates increase with marijuana use. THC may interfere with the passage of nutrients from the placenta to the fetus. Marijuana use may restrict the normal growth of sperm-producing cells in males.

6. Immunity. Research on immunological deficiencies has revealed a lower level of lymphocytes and other substances related to disease in marijuana smokers.

Research Pinpoints How Marijuana Affects The Brain

One of the newest advances in drug abuse research is the discovery that special areas of the brain are directly affected by marijuana. Known as cannabinoid receptors, they can help scientists map out the drug's entry points into the brain.

Dr. Miles Herkenham, a physiological psychologist at the National Institute of Mental Health, reported that marijuana receptors are concentrated in areas of the brain that govern the motor system and memory. Dr. Herkenham states that the localization of the receptors helps explain the psychoactive effects of marijuana as reported in humans and observed in animals, such as alteration of short term memory, drowsiness and reduced attention span.

Observation of Drug Reactions

Observations are helpful in determining which drug is causing the toxic reaction. Hallucinogens such as LSD and mescaline generally produce dilated pupils and hyperactive reflexes. Street stimulants such as cocaine, methamphetamine (crank), and crack are apt to cause increased motor activity, excessive sweating, rapid pulse rate and paranoia. The opiates (morphine, heroin) cause a contraction of the pupils if taken alone. Marijuana causes a redness of the conjunctiva (internal portion of the eyelid and associated attachment to the eyeball), but no dilation of the pupils. Thus, the "red eye" may be a result of the smoking of marijuana. (Note: most information regarding drug reactions and treatments are included in individual chapters, Ed.)

Tobacco Chewing

Is the Chewing of Tobacco a Harmless Habit that Avoids Undesirable Effects of Smoking?

Investigators started with an exploration of the existing medical literature and found numerous reports that chewing tobacco had caused cancers of the mouth and throat as well as other parts of the body. Abnormal tissue growth in the mouth tends to be *raised and light colored.* If you chew, and changes occur on your gums, see a dermatologist. Make the intelligent decision, find out what it is. Dental decay, inflammation of the gums, prenatal effects on unborn babies when pregnant women chewed tobacco, and disturbances of the immune system were also described.

The responses of an inventory of high school students in Arkansas revealed various bits of information about their chewing tobacco habits. Nearly 100 percent of the students had begun chewing during the last 5 years, and the overwhelming majority were increasing its use to a daily habit. Seventy–one percent of the chewers admitted they also drank alcohol and 72 percent said they did not smoke tobacco. The dipping of snuff and the chewing of tobacco is on a dramatic rise among the young people of the United States and poses a challenge that should not be neglected.

Nic-Addiction

The Surgeon General of the United States has declared all-out war on tobacco use. Calling cigarettes and all other forms of tobacco "addicting in the same sense as are drugs such as heroin and cocaine." The report destroyed the last argument of the tobacco industry and its supporters that smoking may be a nasty habit, but it is one which people choose of their own free wills.

Tobacco's main pusher in Congress, said he'd never heard of a guy going home and beating his wife after buying a pack of cigarettes. Well, sifting through the ashes in the fireplace looking for a long butt isn't exactly an unheard of ritual. It usually takes place when someone runs out of smokes early one morning. The fireplace search for hidden "butts" isn't exactly free will, nor is any addiction. Drug seeking behavior begins when the reserves are close to being depleted.

The United States government says nicotine is addictive. The tobacco industry says it isn't. You decide. Is smoking just a harmless little vice that anybody can quit whenever they want? *Nicorette gum makes it easier.* In addition, nicotine stick-on patches are being tested to more effectively help

16

smokers quit the habit. The patches deliver a constant supply of nicotine through the skin rather than delivering an uneven supply from the chewing gum.

How to Stop Smoking

Donald Fredrickson, the medical director of the Smoking Control Program of the New York City Department of Health offers the following guideline to smokers who wish to quit. A smoking record is only a part of overall report published in the NTRDA Bulletin.

Keeping a smoking record is one of the most powerful psychological weapons for the smoker. First, wrap a piece of paper around the pack of cigarettes on which to keep records for two weeks. (Four column headings can be put on the paper, entitled: time of day; activity being carried on while smoking; mood or feelings at the time, and cigarette value). The subject can then smoke as much as wanted for the next two weeks, but for each cigarette smoked, the procedure must be completed. A notation must be entered on the paper, the time of day, what the person is doing, mood or feelings while smoking (i.e. bored, angry, tense), and the smoker must then assign a value to the cigarette on a rating scale of I, II, III, IV, or V. The cigarettes that are indispensable are rated I. The least important ones, the ones that you could take or leave, are rated V. All other cigarettes are rated between I and V. No exceptions should be made. Every cigarette must be noted. If the record cannot be kept then the cigarette is not to be smoked. Even a puff from someone else's cigarette must be recorded.

Analyzing the record is the next step. Smokers look at their records to discover what they have found out about themselves. Under this plan the smoker usually discovers the following: simply by keeping the record the smoker has begun to reduce the habit and the first cigarettes to go are the V's, IV's, and III's. The smoker discovers that all cigarettes are not alike, and are used for different reasons. Smoking is partly automatic, that some cigarettes are lighted with little awareness of what is going on. The cigarette smoker discovers that there are strong associations between certain activities and cigarettes, such as drinking coffee, having a cocktail, or relaxing after meals. Associations may be discovered also between smoking and certain feelings, such as tension, boredom, or a sense of well being. Smokers usually find out that only three or four cigarettes in a day are truly important. Buy only one package of cigarettes at a time, never a carton. Don't light up.

Changes Over Time in Student Reactions to the Surgeon General's Report on Smoking and Health

Until the Surgeons General's recent declaration that nicotine is a highly addictive and dangerous drug, avoidance of the subject of nicotine dependence has been rampant. Due to a complex system of denial, economics, and fear, nicotine addiction has slipped through the cracks of alcohol and drug treatment programs. And there it has remained, despite irrefutable evidence that tobacco, in one form or another, is the killer of all time. Consider these figures:

1. Deaths from cocaine, heroin, and other addictions: 15 a day
2. Deaths from alcoholism-related illnesses: 350 a day.
3. Deaths from smoking-induced diseases: 1,000 a day.

Most drugs, alcohol, the opiates, cocaine, speed, can eventually kill their users. All totalled, not nearly as many addicts will die from the effects of these "traditional" drugs as from the drug nicotine. To make matters worse, tobacco and alcohol, are legal killers. The slow onset of smoking's deadly side effects makes avoidance easy. With other drugs, the negative consequences of usage come on quickly but are frequently reversible. Tobacco doesn't show its hand for years, but when it does, it's usually too late to change in time.

Summary

The effects of being addicted to drugs are difficult to predict. People are different. Susceptibilities vary. Dosages can range from harmless to deadly. Knowledge of potential effects may be as diverse as complete ignorance to complex technical understanding.

Prescription and non prescription drugs have been classified into five major categories by the Controlled Substances Act. Drugs with a high potential for abuse and dependence are tightly restricted and are listed as Schedule 1 compounds.

It is unrealistic to assume that a drug will produce the same effect when used with another drug. One drug may markedly influence the action of another. It is difficult to predict how a particular person may react to a drug. Individual differences in rates of metabolism can vary tremendously.

Since the mother will house the fetus for approximately 40 weeks, maternal health is of utmost importance. The genetic inheritance may be normal, but the embryo may be affected by drugs, or by other factors. If normal development is interfered with, a defect will result. Every type of substance passes from the maternal blood to the fetal blood during pregnancy.

Fetal alcohol syndrome (FAS) is among the leading known causes of birth defects with accompanying mental retardation, and the only preventable one. The amount of alcohol that can be safely consumed has not been established. The use of cocaine or similar drugs is also not advisable by the expectant mother.

Most drugs, alcohol, the opiates, cocaine, speed, can eventually kill their users. Not nearly as many addicts will die from the effects of "traditional" drugs as from the drug nicotine. The harmful effects of chewing tobacco are also introduced. Psychological and physical changes brought about by the use of Phencyclidine, LSD and marijuana are dose related. These substances can produce hallucinogenic reactions.

Self-Test

1. A leading symptom that may be caused by the drug LSD resembles: (A) anorexia nervosa; (B) schizophrenia; C) depressive illness; D) insomnia; E) none of the foregoing.

2. When drugs are used by a pregnant woman the greatest damage to the unborn baby is most likely to occur: (A) late; (B) about half-way through; (C) early; (D) at any stage; (E) not at all.

3. Drugs given to a pregnant woman are not handled well by the unborn child because of: (A) immature kidney function; (B) a lack of sufficient liver enzymes; (C) a deficiency of oxygen; (D) lack of development of various body organs; (E) all of the foregoing.

4. The fetal alcohol syndrome is a set of symptoms that: (A) appear in pregnant women who drink heavily during pregnancy; (B) a disorder of alcoholic fathers; (C) develops only in babies who have both an alcoholic father and mother; (D) show up in babies of mothers who drink alcohol during pregnancy; (E) have no connection with parents.

5. When cocaine is used by a pregnant woman the baby: (A) may be lost by abortion; (B) has a greater startle response than those infants whose mothers did not use the drug during pregnancy; (C) can suffer prenatal strokes because of fluctuations in blood pressure affecting the fragile vessels, rendering the child potentially paralyzed at birth.; (D) will swallow the drug after birth whenever the mother uses coke as it passes into breast milk.; (E) all of the foregoing.

6. Reactions to PCP may lead to a mistaken diagnosis of: (A) atherosclerosis; (B) schizophrenia; (C) diabetes; (D) congenital mental retardation.

7. If a patient is suffering from a severe reaction to phencyclidine and is mistakenly treated for schizophrenia there may be: (A) no damage; (B) a dangerous slowing of the heart rate; (C) severe elevation of the blood pressure; (D) a fatal outcome; (E) onset of epileptic seizures.

8. The harmful effects of tobacco are best avoided by: (A) chewing the drug; (B) smoking less; (C) smoking cigars or pipes; (D) using snuff; (E) none of the foregoing.

Answers: (1) B; (2) C; (3) E; (4) D; (5) E; (6) B; (7) D; (8) E

Notes

1. "Reprinted from the PharmChem Newsletter c. 1988, PharChem Laboratories, Inc., by permission."
2. Source: Drug Enforcement Administration.
3. Source: U.S. Food and Drug Administration.

Bibliography

1. Gold, Mark S., M.D. *Wonder Drugs: How They Work.* 223 pp. Pocket Books, New York, New York, 1987.
2. Boskind-White, Marlene and William C. White. *Bulimarexia.* 284 pp. W.W. Norton and Co., New York, New York, 1987.
3. Kaufman, Joel and Linda Rabinowitz-Dagi, M.D., Joan Levin, Phyllis McCarthy, Sidney Wolfe, M.D., Eve Bargmann, M.D. & the Public Citizen Health Research Group. *Over The Counter Pills That Don't Work.* 301 pp. Pantheon Books, New York, New York, 1983.
4. Sheehan, David V., M.D. *The Anxiety Disease.* 190 pp. Bantam Books, New York, New York, 1983.
5. Peele, Stanton. *How Much is too Much.* 140 pp. Prentice-Hall, Inc., Englewood Clifts, New Jersey, 1981.

Alcohol Abuse and Alcoholism

Introduction

Alcohol is one of the most abused drugs in the world. Because the consumption of alcohol is legal for most adults, conflicts with society ordinarily develop only after an individual has consumed so much ethanol that behavior is affected. The person becomes a hazard to others, such as in the case of drunken driving, physical assault, or some other type of dangerous or socially undesirable behavior.

Most people who consume alcohol in moderation can drink with relative safety and the drug does not create substantial problems in their lives. Others drink differently. Some people suffer problems from the first drink, and others after years of drinking. The alcoholic shows a loss of control. Somewhere between normal and pathological drinking, there is a line that a drinker may pass over and never be able to return. Alcohol makes us less shy, creates a feeling of fitting in, enhances our social ability, and makes us feel more whole. If we find that it works, most likely we will look for the same feelings again. Patterns develop.

The common theme that brings alcohol, tobacco, and drug users into the same category is that they cannot leave them alone under ordinary circumstances, even if health is being impaired. However, if the incentive is great enough, people who use these drugs can be helped and may abandon their use.

High Addiction Potential

Alcoholism is accepted by the medical profession as an illness in itself, but it causes other illnesses, unemployment, broken families, and many other undesirable social effects. In fact, it is well known that alcohol outranks all

21

other drugs as a social problem in terms of abuse, availability, death, disease, destruction, shattered lives and financial costs.

Think about these four questions. 1) Is the use of alcohol essential to functioning normally? 2) Do you crave for alcohol after a period of abstinence? 3) Do you need to drink more? 4) Do you come from an addictive family background? Certain people's natural biochemical balance makes them react more intensely to the drug. They get more pleasure from it, the feelings are more acute, they feel more than what others experience All four questions point towards dependency.

On the other hand, social drinking is thought to be acceptable, relaxing, and innocuous by the great majority of people. It seems obvious that alcohol doesn't cause alcoholism but some combination of physiological and emotional factors do.

Treatment of the alcoholic may lead to physical withdrawal symptoms that are undoubtedly related to failures of therapy. If the drinker responded to rehabilitation, there would be no need for further treatment. Although many drinkers succeed in stopping their drinking, their basic personalities and physiologies remain unchanged. Those alcoholics who drop out of treatment programs are most likely to have severe disruptions of their interpersonal relationships. Thus, treatment for alcoholism involves both physical and psychological factors of significance.

Compulsive, Addictive Personality Problems

The biochemical properties of alcohol must be considered in order to understand the effects on the brain. Alcohol has the properties of both glucose and ether. Glucose is an energy food while ether is an anesthetic. Alcohol produces heat energy, but provides virtually no nutrition. The alcoholic tends to be ill-fed but is anesthetized by drink, and may be unaware of hunger.

The most significant changes that alcohol produces in the body comes from its anesthetic effects. An anesthetic produces its results by interfering with normal glucose oxidation. It is a depressant drug that acts directly on nervous tissue, and the degree of disturbance is greatest on the highest and most complex brain centers. Therefore, the very part of the brain that suffers the most from alcoholism is that part which controls the highest cerebral functions of will power, judgment, inhibition and control—namely the frontal lobes. The drinker feels free of responsibilities and anxieties. This is the initial basis for psychological dependence.

Personality changes are shown in symptoms such as: rationalization of drinking, pathologic lying, infantile behavior, poor judgment, hostility, emotional instability, defiance, denial of illness, and lack of insight. Social pressures soon lead to secretive drinking, work is neglected and financial difficulties add to the disintegration of personality.

22

The alcoholic starts drinking more and will drink longer than the nonalcoholic. Few alcoholics intend to drink too much, but once the alcohol is in the system there is an immediate paralysis of the control centers of the brain, and the alcoholic is helpless to stop after the first drink. Sometimes an alcoholic can be fooled and may get away with a couple of drinks. The term alcohol abuse reminds me of terminology describing someone throwing an expensive bottle of Champagne against a wall.

Drinking might occur on a flight to a business meeting. An alcoholic will think, "I got away with it this time, maybe I can again." The pattern will always go from a lesser amount to a greater amount. The alcoholic is helpless after the first drink. The second drink may not occur until a month later. The first drink may not bring catastrophic results, therefore temporarily deceiving and drawing the drinker to another attempt at controlled drinking.

The most common type of alcoholic is the reactive type. This type of person is unstable, emotionally immature, and insecure. Alcohol is consumed in increasing amounts as a tranquilizer for relief of anxiety, and finally the drinker loses control. The alcoholic drinks as a substitute for obligations, and as an escape from intolerable situations that cannot be faced. The typical female alcoholic tends to be affected by a particular situation. This could be a death in the family, postpartum depression, or a deteriorating family relationship.

Another group comprises purposeful, deliberate alcoholics who drink for a specific effect when rejected or lonely. Another motivation may be self-destruction or the expression of hostility against a spouse, boss, or other person.

After sustained, excessive drinking, usually over a period of years, organic factors occur that cause the beginning of brain damage, with impairment of judgment and emotional self-control. At this stage, the alcoholic must be protected from hurting themselves further. Only then can reconstructive emotional and psychological rehabilitation be effective. The addicted alcoholic usually does not really wish to give up alcohol. Brain damage prevents acceptance of the facts and denies the alcoholism.

General Conclusions, Central Nervous System (CNS) Depressants

- Chronic use can be harmful to the body
- Can cause death by respiratory depression
- Has properties of tolerance and cross tolerance
- Can cause reverse tolerance
- Are physically addicting

Tolerance is defined as the need to increase the dose in order to achieve the desired effect, and withdrawal produces characteristic signs and symptoms when a drug is suddenly removed. Cells cannot function normally until the body becomes able to produce or use its own biochemicals properly. Until then, there is the withdrawal period with symptoms varying in onset and duration for each drug.

Cross tolerance tends to develop among drugs in the same class. Drugs have been grouped together in Chapter 1. Once you have acquired tolerance to a psychoactive drug, you will have acquired equivalent tolerance to other related drugs.

Physical dependency and withdrawal are explained in greater detail in Chapter Nine. There are two kinds of dependency: physical and psychological. In physical dependency, the substance becomes biochemically necessary for body cells to function normally. The sedative-hypnotics and narcotics produce physical dependency. The stimulants are believed to cause a primarily psychological dependency.

Chronic use can be harmful to the body. Alcohol is toxic to every cell of the body and it is a powerful immunosuppressive drug. Degeneration of the brain occurs from the heavy consumption of alcohol. Personality changes are extensive. The temporary period of amnesia is a significant early symptom of alcoholism. Research studies show that alcohol interferes with the capacity of the brain to pay attention to several different things at once. Thinking is impaired, drunk or sober.

Theories of Addiction

What do we mean by disease? Dorlands Medical Dictionary, 26th Ed., states: "Any deviation from or interruption of the normal structure or function of any part, organ, or system of the body that is manifested by a characteristic set of signs and symptoms and whose etiology, pathology, and prognosis may be known or unknown. "The disease" is termed by DSM-III-R in the category "psychoactive substance abuse disorders." That's a diagnostic code physicians write on an insurance form. Insurance companies are not concerned with theory, they just require knowledge as to the nature of the problem. The problem has many different names, all used in describing a certain entity.

We needed the "disease model" of alcoholism badly to help those caught in the powerful cycle of physiological addiction. It had clear messages: 1) you had to stop drinking because it would destroy you; 2) you had no control over the inevitable biological progression; and 3) the only way to save yourself was to stop drinking completely. Some variations of the disease model have oversimplified matters by trying to explain all of human behavior by the unfolding disease process. The pendulum has swung too far, these reduced models based solely on the biological components of addiction invite criticism. Opponents argue this concept just cannot describe the complex social process, family dynamics and interpersonal interactions involved in the onset of alcoholism.

Anytime you have a developing field in which only partial answers are recognized, there will be some disagreement. This applies especially to treatment. Did the problem create the alcoholism or was it vice versa? For one thing, the disease model very usefully permits the alcoholic and others to avoid the guilt that drinking causes, which is one of the continuing sources of addiction. Some alcoholics mention that one important cause of their drinking was the everpresent coping difficulties.

We need the disease concept to account for the physiologic impact of addiction and to mandate abstinence; we need the fellowship of AA to help recovering alcoholics adjust to a life of abstinence. But we also need psychology to help understand what is happening when someone begins to rely on alcohol. If alcoholism is multifactorial in its causes, its treatments must address the entire biopsychosocial continuum of the individual.

What, for example, would we say about a man who drinks at social gatherings in order to overcome his insecurities? By seeking a physical cause for his "alcoholism," we ignore the real cause of his drinking, a lack of confidence about dealing with other people. Because he doesn't drink to the point of unconsciousness, we might refuse to label him an alcoholic. On the other hand, not recognizing the cause of his drinking could readily allow it to grow to more dangerous proportions as the man fails to come to grips with his sense of inadequacy. Once someone start using alcohol as a drug and drinks to forget personal problems, they are gone. The drinker will wake up as a temporary sober person with the same problems as before.

What is truly clear is that some people slip into a state of alcoholism during trying periods in their lives, and they may stay there when there is no prospect of reviving their careers. This observation tells us much about alcoholism, but nothing about a person's inbred and unalterable susceptibility to alcohol.

Alcoholism Runs in Families

Doctor Donald Goodwin, of Washington University in St. Louis, winner of a Jellinek Memorial Award for outstanding contributions to the study of alcohol problems, has concluded that alcoholism has a biological background that involves human heredity.

The conclusions are based on a collaborative analysis of 50 years of cumulative records of admissions to psychiatric hospitals in Denmark. Even when they have been adopted and raised by others, the children of alcoholic parents have a much higher rate of alcoholism than others of non-alcoholic ancestry.

25

This study which started with data covering 5,000 children and 10,000 parents, could not be conducted in the United States because when children are adopted in this country no records are kept of the drinking habits of the biological parents. Thus, needed information is not available.

According to the Danish records, six times as many alcoholic children developed alcoholism when they had alcoholic ancestry compared to non-alcoholic parents.

Doctor Goodwin reports that alcoholism runs so strongly in families that he believes the primary explanation must be that there is a biological predisposition to the illness that is hereditary in origin, but he has no idea or proof of what specific hereditary mechanisms may be involved.

It is difficult to tell what this impressive tendency toward alcoholism involves. It is conceivable that alcoholic parents may transmit stress-susceptible personalities, genetic deficiencies that result in disturbed enzyme systems, or more obscure biological handicaps to the children, but clarification of the relationships between alcoholism and heredity must await further research.

_____ QUOTATION _____

"The biological predisposition to alcoholism may predate the challenge with alcohol."

David Smith, M.D.

Inherited Alcohol Problems

Two different forms of inherited alcohol problems that have distinct genetic and environmental causes have been identified by researchers working together at the National Alcohol Research Center at Washington University in St. Louis (MO) and the Umea University School of Medicine in Umea, Sweden.

One type of alcohol problem is called male-limited because it tends to be passed only from fathers to sons. It is highly hereditary regardless of environment and limited to men whose natural fathers have records of extensive treatment for combined alcohol abuse and criminal behavior.

The other is referred to as milieu-limited because of the role that environment plays in the frequency and severity of its development. It affects both men and women and is usually associated with mild alcohol abuse and minimal criminal behavior on the part of the natural parents.

The research was reported in two separate articles in *Archives of General Psychiatry* (Vol 38, August and September 1981.) The findings are based on an extensive examination of medical and social records of 862 males and 913 females born in Stockholm, Sweden, from 1930 to 1949 and subsequently adopted. Sweden was seen as an ideal site for an adoption study because adoption records are more extensive there than in other countries. The 10-year study began in 1970.

The researchers found that, if the natural parents of adopted children were alcoholic, the children ran a greater risk of becoming problem drinkers despite being raised by nonalcoholic adoptive parents. How-ever if the natural parents were not alcoholic and the adoptive parents were, the risk was not increased.

The male-limited form of alcohol abuse accounted for about 24 percent of the adopted men with alcohol problems. This type of alcohol abuse is probably of hereditary origin rather than adoptive environments. Drinking problems of the fathers of this group began early in life, usually in adolescence. The alcoholic behavior usually interfered with work and marriage and led to crimes of violence such as assault and wife beating.

A much more common type of alcohol problem, the milieu-limited form, affected 76 percent of the men and all the women with alcohol problems whose natural parents had alcoholism. Although susceptibility was hereditary, environmental factors had significant impact on both frequency and severity of the problem.

The biological fathers of these men had a history of heavy drinking that began in their 20s or 30s and gradually progressed to a state of physical dependence in middle age. The fathers were usually able to maintain their jobs and families.

The milder milieu-limited type of alcohol problem also appeared to be inherited by women, most often from their mothers. Among adopted daughters whose natural parents had alcohol problems, from 6.7 to 7.7 percent developed alcoholism. It is apparent that the men were much more susceptible to hereditary-influenced alcoholism. Although both fathers and mothers with mild forms of problems had daughters who became alcoholic, daughters whose mothers had problems stood out as much more susceptible.

Addiction Proneness

Many persons have a proneness to become addicted to drugs. A major problem in the management of the alcoholic during periods of sobriety is to prevent a dependency upon other drugs. *The addictive-prone individual easily slips from one addiction to another.* Emotional problems may certainly contribute to why a person takes drugs, but the mechanism of dependency is mostly biochemical and about 10 percent of our population are predisposed to addictive disease. There is an interrelation of body and mind in the formation and functioning of the body. Alcohol is an addictive drug.

There is irrefutable evidence that the brain chemistry of the alcoholic is different from that of the nonalcoholic. When the alcoholic's brain is invaded by alcohol, it manufactures an opiate more addictive than alcohol itself!

The liver of the normal drinker will metabolize alcohol, converting it into other substances and ending up with CO_2 & H_2O. The liver of the alcoholic metabolizes alcohol differently from that of the nonalcoholic. One of the byproducts, acetaldehyde is produced in higher quantities and consequently remains in the body longer. Acetaldehyde combines with various neurotransmitters in the brain, creating a heroin-like substance called TIQ which many researchers feel is responsible for the addiction. TIQ gathers gradually in the alcoholic brain, subtly increasing a greater dependence on this drug. In other words, alcoholism appears to be a true addiction which involves specific biochemical reactions in the body that lead to the production of heroin-like substances.

Agitation and Sedation, the Hook

Sedative drugs produce similar effects in all mammals. The effects occur at approximately the same time. When any sedative drug is taken, an opposite reaction will also be produced causing agitation. The agitation always outlasts the sedation.

Many social drinkers anticipate the effects of the alcoholic beverage. The drug will impair judgment and emotional self-control, creating a sense of well being and excitement. Most become more convivial. The social drinker usually goes no further, and stops drinking. Most alcoholics will continue drinking until they can no longer walk, express confusing thoughts, pass out and are generally socially rejected. The alcoholic may drink before the party, behave relatively normally while in public, and finish the drinking at home.

Any person who elects to overdrink on occasion, or can't help it will sedate themselves. If intoxication occurs most people will pass out until the blood alcohol levels diminish. Upon awakening, a general feeling of malaise will overshadow your normal vitality. You have just been introduced to the agitation. During this time of discomfort you probably will do some things to alleviate the pain. Since the body is thirsty and dehydrated, it is ap-

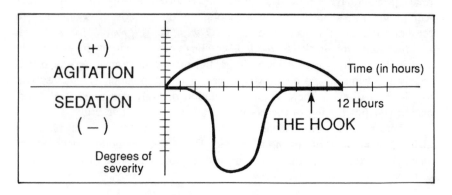

propriate to get some fluids. Aspirin may help. Then, back to sleep. Simple isn't it?

The sad part about the sedation-agitation combination is that too many people begin to treat a drug-induced problem with the same substance or another drug combination. The extended agitation creates "the hook of addiction". Avoid it if you can.

Ethanol in Distilled Spirits, Wine and Beer

The chemical substance that makes all alcoholic beverages intoxicating is ethanol, ethyl alcohol. The concentration of ethanol is the primary intoxicant variable in alcoholic beverages. The proof stated on the bottle is equal to twice the amount of ethanol it contains. Therefore, 50 percent of the proof stated on the bottle is equal to the amount of ethanol it contains. Keep in mind that a shot of 80-proof vodka is 40 percent ethanol. About one ounce of distilled spirits contain about 1/2 ounce ethanol. Remember, distilled spirits and ethanol are not the same. The amount or percentage of ethanol is equal to half the proof indicated on the bottle.

Ninety percent of ethanol is oxidized. This means that the body produces heat and energy by combining alcohol with oxygen and ultimately converting the mixture to water and carbon dioxide. Oxidation proceeds at a constant rate. Time is the important factor in eliminating alcohol from the body.

An average serving of most alcoholic beverages contains about the same amount of ethanol. A four ounce glass of wine and a 12-ounce can of beer each contain about 1/2 ounce of ethanol. Wine contains the higher concentration of ethanol. Both the 12-ounce can of beer and the four ounce glass of wine contain comparable amounts of ethanol. Despite the relatively mild alcoholic reputation, if you drink a lot of beer, you drink considerable amounts of alcohol. So, we may assume the wine is roughly three times as strong as beer. However, since few people stop at four ounces of beer, an "average" serving of beer is as potent as an "average" glass of wine.

There is approximately the same amount of ethanol in a 1-ounce shot of 100-proof distilled spirits, a four ounce glass of wine, and a 12-ounce can of beer. An average serving of each has about the same alcohol content and is almost equally intoxicating. When a person drinks alcohol at a faster rate than his or her body can oxidize it intoxication will occur, if enough alcohol is accumulated. Remember, drinking does not have to cause intoxication. People can drink alcoholic beverages at rates or in amounts that do not necessarily cause drunkenness.

Withdrawal From Extensive Alcohol Abuse

The unpleasant symptoms of withdrawal are relieved by alcohol. In this way drinking can extend through the greater part of the day. The alcoholic often has a reduced tolerance to the effects of alcohol and may become irrational and may experience periods of amnesia. The blackout, or temporary period of amnesia, is a significant early symptom. It usually means that brain disease is present or near at hand. Impairment of memory will occur. Physiological reactions include withdrawal reactions, blackouts, and severe hangovers. Episodes of delirium or convulsions may occur.

Withdrawal from alcohol takes time. It is best treated by not consuming alcohol as this act may simply put off the in-evitable. Rest, liquids and time are needed. If symptoms are severe, medical supervision should provide the best protection for the patient. Anti-convulsant medication could be started and one of the tranquilizers can help alleviate tremors. There are three basic objectives: 1) relieving agitation, 2) correcting dehydration, and 3) preventing complications.

There are four key elements in the medical treatment of a person who is having alcohol withdrawal symptoms.

1. The onset of symptoms from withdrawal must be recognized and properly treated to reduce the more severe complications that may result in death. An idiopathic grand mal seizure, occurring without a known cause, can cause death.

2. Appropriate sedation of the victim of alcohol withdrawal symptoms should be achieved with drugs that have a rapid action, moderate duration of effects, and anti-convulsive properties. These drugs must not further depress the heart rate or respiration.

3. The extent of fluid loss or retention must be accurately determined. It has long been assumed that chronic alcoholics are in a state of dehydration during withdrawal when, in fact, they may be retaining a surplus of body fluids. For example the face may become swollen. During delirium tremens, if such a condition is present, there may be fluid loss from the sweat and evaporation, breathing off of water vapor from the lungs and loss of fluid from the stomach and intestines in the form of diarrhea and vomiting. Fluid loss from the skin may be substantial.

4. Intensive follow-up of the patient in delirium tremens is especially important. DT's may include both visual and auditory hallucinations. Pseudo hallucinations may consist of annoying little random noises, and or visual disturbances fluctuating from seeing spots to a silver lizard darting across the floor.

A number of biochemical byproducts of alcohol metabolism and drinking are acetaldehyde, acetate and methanol. Consumption of ethanol inhibits the metabolism of methanol, probably resulting in its progressive accumulation in body fluids and tissues. The most severe withdrawal signs and symptoms occur when methanol concentrations are high and blood ethanol concentrations approached zero. The drinker will continue to appear intoxicated while alcohol levels steadily decrease to zero level.

Most alcoholics cut down on coffee, tea and cola when they realize their withdrawal symptoms become much worse.

Degeneration of Body Systems

Heavy drinking of alcohol must continue about 10 years before the liver is damaged and it has long been recognized that the amount of drink consumed daily will be related to the extent of liver damage. It also has been found that for the liver to be injured severely the alcohol intake must amount to about 50 percent of the total calories consumed.

Normally the liver metabolizes fats, however when alcohol is introduced into the body, the preferred fuel becomes alcohol. Fats begin to accumulate in the liver. The liver can and does regenerate to a point. If the alcoholic liver is not irreversibly damaged and the alcoholic stops drinking, the tissue can heal. If large areas of dead cells along with fatty degeneration and fibrosis exist, regeneration prospects are limited. Severe death of liver cells with overgrowth of connective tissue indicates cirrhosis (liver failure). When the drinker becomes ill or gets intoxicated upon consumption of a lesser amount of the drug than usual, it may be a sign of a partially non-functioning liver. The phenomenon is known as reverse tolerance.

Alcohol has a direct toxic effect on the intestinal tract. About 20 percent of the alcohol you consume is absorbed through your stomach and the other 80 percent is absorbed from the small intestine. Alcohol is absorbed faster from the small intestine than from the stomach. Cramping, abdominal pain and diarrhea are especially apt to occur after heavy drinking. Bleeding in the stomach and small intestines has been known to take place. Alcohol causes a drug-induced intestinal malabsorption condition. Recovery from the latter usually occurs when the drinker eats a complete diet even if drinking continues. The absorbtion of salt, and certain vitamins, most notably of the B group, is impaired in the chronic alcoholic.

Alcohol also causes an accumulation of certain fats in the blood and this condition is often associated with inflammation of the pancreas and severe abdominal pain. Sometimes calcification of the pancreas occurs. In alcoholic cirrhosis, the damaged liver is related to an impaired protein synthesis and low levels of albumin.

Amino acids, the building blocks of proteins, are adversely affected in both the blood and other body fluids. A variety of imaging techniques and measures of cardiac muscle strength have shown that alcoholics were more likely than others to have weak heart muscles and evidence of car-

31

diomyopathy, a condition that causes the heart to pump poorly and erratically.

Free Will and the Corpse of Determinism

_____QUOTATION_____

"Like the Phoenix, free will is birthed out of the ashes of the corpse of determinism, for out of the determinant course of physical events free-will arises and takes wing. When new knowledge is acquired, new cognitive constructs are formed creating the possibility of freedom of choice."

Dawn Jones, CSU, San Jose

Determinism, the notion that all actions of the mind and body are determined by prior "events," presupposes a rigid cause and effect relationship. In opposition to this, the free will doctrine maintains that the individual has the power to choose.

Although neither line of these reasoning processes is incorrect, certain basic and necessary components are omitted. Human beings process, manipulate, reflect on, and make decisions regarding information acquired through the senses, thus humankind accumulates knowledge. Out of this knowledge emerges the capacity of the human being to make choices. Decisions affecting future behavior and events which otherwise would be determined and limited by the previously existing cognitive data are made possible.

Many theories have emerged in an effort to explain the phenomena of alcoholism, however there is little consensus at this time regarding the genesis of this condition.

READING

"As far back as I can remember there were forces shaping the course and quality of my life: parents, peers, siblings, teachers, judges, and husbands, to name a few. However, by far and away the most dominant, tenacious, and unrelenting force I have experienced was not another human being, it was a drug called alcohol. The determining forces of alcoholism operated in my life for 20 years.

Before I awoke each morning the pre-determined behavior and events existed and prevailed. There was no thought, no decision, no option of what to do. I was not aware of any positive alternative. There was only one thing to do, have a drink. Likewise, with the first drink, everything that followed was then determined by that first drink. This undeniably and clearly is a classic example of determinism. I had no choice to take the first drink or not, given the nature of the disorder and the limited scope of the information from which I was operating.

Life was a circular chain reaction. There was no hope of anything being different. As long I remained in this limited state of existence, with no new knowledge, the determining power of the ailment prevailed. This course would inevitably lead to death as a result of chronic alcoholism.

The pain of this subsistence eventually drove me to a hospital where I was exposed to new data. This provided new material for understanding, and from this insight was birthed new alternatives. These psychological and behavioral alternatives were not formerly available for consideration because my thinking processes were confined within the boundaries established by my limited knowledge and alcoholic disorder.

As long as the malady was in control there were no choices. Only after the acquisition of new knowledge and increased consciousness could free will or a power to choose emerge. Now, for the first time, there exists the choice to take the first drink or abstain. My life both today and tomorrow have been radically enhanced because of this new freedom.

From this powerful experience I have come to respect the tremendous value, without which I am destined to be controlled by circumstances, people, inner drives, and even illness, rather than participation in the freedom of choice. It is this new knowledge that liberates us from the bondage of determinism."

Paula Douglas

To Paula, who became a rose,
Human beings are at their very best when things are at their worst. ∎

Symptoms of Alcoholism

The fundamental problem with alcohol is not physical, it's behavioral. People who drink too much act differently and the alcoholic goes through a complete personality change. The symptoms of alcoholism would include some or all of the following:

1. blackouts, can't remember what has occurred while under the influence
2. loss of control
3. hangovers that interfere with activities

33

4. can't predict amount, frequency, duration or effect of drinking
5. gulping and sneaking drinks
6. drinking alone at inappropriate times
7. relief drinking (to calm down, sleep, alleviate nervous tension)
8. lies and excuses rationalizing reasons for drinking (an alibi system)
9. needing a drink after a period of deprivation
10. drinking alone to hide the frequency and amount
11. Trying to change the pattern of drinking in an attempt that this will help control the problem i.e., exchanging hard liquor for beer or pot. For an alcoholic, that's like changing deck space on the Titanic
12. anti-social behavior
13. loss of friends, jobs and families
14. protect the supply by hiding it
15. resentful and unreasonable
16. missing work or school, lateness (absenteeism)
17. binges and hospitals
18. bumps and bruises from falling into things
19. increased or decreased tolerance for alcohol
20. increased reliance on alcohol

Alcoholic Blackouts

The use of the term "blackout" in connection with alcohol consumption is unfortunate because many people confuse the term with "passing out" or unconsciousness. The term "blackout" should be more explicitly defined as the forgetting of things done while drinking. Drinkers may carry on conversations and engage in various activities without any memory of these events the next day. There is no loss of consciousness but there is a loss of memory. Most drinkers who have experienced a blackout behave almost the same as during periods of comparable intoxication in which no memory loss occurred. Sexual experiences are common, without the drinker having any recollection of such events.

The most dramatic blackout often involves travel. Many drinkers find themselves in places where they have no recollection of getting there. To have negotiated such distances, the person must have had certain control over their faculties.

One type of blackout has a definite beginning, terminates with a feeling of "lost time" and is seldom followed by a return of memory. Another type involves a loss of memory for events until they were remembered spontaneously or remembered after being brought to the attention of the drinker.

Alcohol Addiction in Young Men

A Senior Research Associate of the Department of Psychiatry, Queen Elizabeth Hospital in Birmingham, England reports a study of young male alcoholics in relation to their drinking history.

All of these young men were hospitalized and asked to recall the age at which they had their first drink. The range was from 5 to 21 years, but the average was sightly over 15 years. Regular drinking began on the average of two years later and excessive drinking had developed at approximately 20 years on the average. A table of events in the drinking history of these young alcoholics and the percentage who experienced the events is as follows:

Events	Percentage
Drinking began to take precedence over other activities	100
Amnesias (Blackouts) began to increase	100
Drunkenness in the daytime	90
Loss of appetite	85
Unable to stop drinking after once beginning	83
Drop in efficiency at work	80
Suicidal thoughts or impulses	80
Neglect of food because of spending money on alcohol	78
Drinking to get relief from tension	78
Drinking in the morning	73
Drinking for adequate social performance	70
Drinking every day	70
Debts were incurred because of drinking	53
Unsuccessful attempts were made to stop drinking	53
Loss of a job because of drinking	50
Breakup of a family because of drinking	50
Actual attempt to commit suicide	45
Wife or girl friend takes over more of the responsibilities	40
Drinking of cheap wines	40
Tolerance to alcohol diminishes	38
Development of delirium tremens	35
Attendance at Alcoholics Anonymous meetings	23

Basic Characteristics of Addiction

1. Compulsion to use mood altering drugs.
2. Loss of control over the use of these drugs.
3. Continue to use despite adverse consequences.
4. Possible genetic predisposition.

5. Family and social problems due to drug use.
6. Attempts at control over use of drugs.
7. Possibility of relapse after rehabilitation.

Learning Theory

Normal people learn from negative experiences and don't tend to repeat them. The alcoholic repeats negative behavior, usually not learning in a lifetime.

When I was about ten years old my dad came home with a Christmas tree. The wooden stand had not been attached. We worked together to nail on the base. I remember holding the nail. My dad held the hammer. Obviously, I was nervous. The hammer hit my fingers. It wasn't anybody's fault. The incident imprinted itself in my memory. People have since tempted me to hold tacks, and other types of nails for their convenience. However, that was the last nail I ever held for anybody else. Normally people learn, and avoid negative experiences.

The alcoholic believes they are just *off track* and that if they just drink a little different next time, everything will work out. The drinker fails to see that they are living in a van parked across from a bar, have no bathroom facilities, food, clean clothing or friends. You might see this as an abnormal learning pattern or the sunken garden variety of addictive diseases.

_____ QUOTATION _____
"We hold certain social beliefs about alcohol in this country, and one is that if you drink you become less responsible for what you do. I like to call it the "grand excuse"; because taken to the limit, individuals under the influence of alcohol would have a blanket excuse for everything."

Diane K. Steed

Systematic Suicide

Society will produce its own conflicting and confusing pressures. We can choose to react or not. We can make a decision. But we are also human. Therefore all decisions are subjective and will change. Whenever we are depressed, whenever we are deeply upset, the central cause is rejection of acceptance. Suddenly we become angry at the first person or object that walks in the door. It's a big issue. Or we think we are angry at one another. The fact is, we are just irritated by the circumstances. No one likes to admit being upset by trivial matters, so we act as if we're mad about some big thing. Simple reality needs acceptance.

So, sometimes we let the little things do us in. Common things. The sock phantom strikes again. You're clothing gets stuck in a zipper. You can't find your keys. Sometimes, it's the big things. Parenting seems to rank next to leprosy, at times. Choices, responsibilities, jobs and expectations are all pressures we experience. Almost any time that we are upset, the problem is within, and it hurts all the more when we accept that.

Whenever you look at the sunset, or dawn, or the seashore life seems to come into focus. Recreation and variety is meant to "re-energize" ourselves.

Cycles of Addictive Behavior

The "Cycle of Addiction" is most often initiated by negative interpersonal feelings or idealistic goals. When we place our expectations too high, the actual results can produce disappointment and hurt. Anger may follow. Often anger is stored in the form of resentment. People, who have a so-called "short fuse," exploding in periodic rage without provocation, have been storing resentments. Anger and resentment are two emotions the alcoholic cannot afford to keep. The target of the anger must be identified and dealt with directly. Anger can be self-defeating. The feelings typically progress to "acting out" behavior which can be a form of relief.

The alcoholic may automatically believe he or she is no good, and "act out". This form of behavior is self-destructive and can involve the use of alcohol, drugs, food, spending, sexual promiscuity or other things. Prior to reacting, the person needs to associate the feelings with the automatic thought. Most people will handle anger in a constructive way, understanding their feelings and tying their emotions into specific situations and issues. If the behavior is destructive, most people will feel guilty. Guilt can lead to depression. Setbacks can reinforce negative interpersonal feelings, confirming the illusion that the person is a failure. It's a psychological set-up.

ANECDOTE

For example, upon arriving home your two small children grab your legs, demanding attention. You are tired and irritable. Your husband is not home. You cook and play and wash and read a bedtime story. It takes quite an effort.

Your husband left a cheesecake in the refrigerator. You eat an average slice. You feel a little guilty, since you've been trying to lose 20 pounds. The diet has been ruined, you think. In reality, only one slice of cheesecake has been eaten. But, perfectionistic attitudes influence you to eat the rest of the cake. It's always easier to fail the second time. One ten minute eating binge compromised your personal goals. Negative feelings return. So may self-destructive behavior. Objectives may not be reached.

In the foregoing situation, a baby sitter should have been hired. The evening could have been converted into dinner out and a movie. Being aware of fatigue and irritability, should have prompted you to change this dangerous situation before it got out of hand. The day could have been salvaged. *Know personal limitations, be aware of how to live and deal with conflict.*

Characteristics of an Addictive Experience

The addictive cycle makes clear the characteristics of an involvement with a drug which define that relationship as an addiction. These characteristics also tell us what kind of experience can be addictive. The hallmarks of an addictive experience are as follows: 1) It eradicates awareness. To create the addiction cycle, a drug experience must eliminate a person's sense of pain by lessening awareness of what is troubling the individual; 2) It hurts other involvements. The addiction cycle worsens when a drug experience makes a person less concerned about other responsibilities. The person then turns increasingly toward the drug experience as the one source of gratification in life; 3) It lowers self-esteem. The biggest casualty of an addictive experience is the addict's regard for him or her self; 4) There is nothing pleasurable about the addiction cycle. A popular misconception about drug addiction is that an addict takes a drug for pleasure. Alcoholics are escape artists.

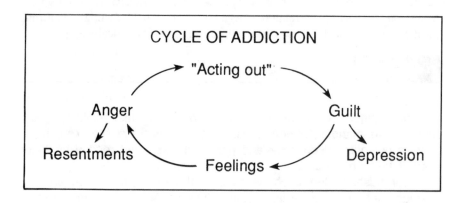

CYCLE OF ADDICTION

"Acting out"

Anger   Guilt

Resentments   Depression

Feelings

For, as Steven Vincent Benet expressed it:

> Life is not lost by dying! Life is
> lost
> Minute by minute, day by
> dragging day,
> In all the thousand, small,
> uncaring ways.

Mothers Against Drunk Driving

MADD was started by Candy Lightner in November 1980, following a tragic accident resulting in the death of her daughter Cari in Fairfax, California. The organization was her way to help protect other innocent victims and became a constructive way for Mrs. Lightner to release her anger. She was responsible for over 100 pieces of new legislation in California during the first year of its organization.

The goal of MADD is "to never meet again," according to Mrs. Jackie Masso, first president of the Santa Clara County chapter in California. The working goals are legislation, victim assistance, and public education. The organization consists of both men and women. MADD stands for Mothers Against Drunk Driving. They are not against the individual; but, they are against the behavior. MADD is not opposed to the drinking of alcoholic beverages. MADD is making a statement about social responsibility, neither condoning or condemning social activity. The anguish of a victim leaves an even deeper impression. Some mistakes are irreversible, and driving drunk is one of them.

Having to deal with a handicap full-time, everyday from something that you didn't even have anything to do with is only a small part of what being a victim is all about. The emotional and mental anguish, the pain and anger that never go away are part of it.

The most incredible fact presented by MADD is the prospect of one out of every two persons becoming directly affected by a drunk driver. Someone in your family, a close friend or relative will be arrested or suffer personal damage due to a drunk driver. The frequency of this even exceeds the rates for cancer in our overall population. And cancer is a disease; not an "act of choice" as in the case of the drunk driver. At least the drinker makes a conscious (at some point) decision to overindulge and drive and then inflicts that choice upon others.

—————————————— QUOTATION ——————————————

"One of the first things I would want is revenge. I'm surprised more people don't act like vigilantes, and take the law into their own hands. How can they seek justice when our laws only sen-

39

*tence offenders to approximately 10 years for vehicular
homicide. Personally, I would like them executed. Drunk drivers
are not prejudiced, they'll hurt or kill any race, sex or age that
gets in their way. Once this happens you're not left with much.
They have destroyed your life in some way in just a few split
seconds. Whether it be killing a family member or injuring yourself, your life will never be the same. What gives them the right
to destroy what is so precious to you?"*

Anonymous

About 50 percent of traffic accident deaths involve drinking, but a drunken driver is not necessarily an alcoholic. Intoxication is the reason for more arrests than any other crime.

Marijuana and Driving Performance

An editor of a Canadian medical journal reports that research around the world carries the strong implication that cannibas does impair driving skills and that the lessening of ability may persist for a surprising length of time.

There is very definite proof that cannibas reduces driving skills. Braking time slows 20 to 66 percent, according to dosage, after cannibas use. In comparing alcohol with marijuana, it was concluded that equal impairment was evident, but in some respects cannibas was more handicapping than alcohol. One other finding among the investigators was that the response to cannibas was more erratic than with alcohol.

Scientists have found that a slower response to sound in either direction occurs with cannibas.. Illusions also occur and sudden flights of ideas cause confusion and anxiety in new situations. Emotional changes, fatigue and a lack of ability to concentrate sometimes last as long as 24 hours after smoking marijuana. Responses involving the eye and hand coordination are impaired after taking cannibas. *The more complex a situation became, the slower the responses. Accuracy is also impaired.*

Summary

Alcohol is the most abused drug in the world although most people do not drink to excess. Physicians of today accept alcoholism as a disease in itself. It causes many disturbances such as other illness, loss of employment, broken families and many lifelong problems. There is no body part that is immune to damage by alcohol, but its most critical influence is on the brain. Changes in personality are expressed in many ways, including poor judgment, hostility, emotional instability, defiance, lying, neglect of work obligations, and many other factors. The alcoholic may undergo biochemical chan-

40

ges that are dangerous and life-threatening, both from heavy drinking and the effects of withdrawing from alcohol. Alcoholism has family associations with implications of genetic inheritance. The alcoholic is prone to use drugs which broaden the problems of addiction. Alcoholics have generally started drinking early in life, mostly during adolescence without any comprehension of how the drug can change their lives.

Self-Test

1. The drug that outranks all others as a cause of illnesses, loss of work and breakup of families is: (A) marijuana; (B) cocaine; (C) alcohol; (D) heroin; (E) morphine.

2. The reason why alcoholics are not cured by the cessation of drinking is thought to be because their: (A) fundamental personalities have not changed; (B) physiology is not altered; C) basic genetic susceptibilities remain the same; (D) problems have not been solved; (E) all or any of the foregoing.

3. The most significant changes produced by alcohol in the body involve the: (A) liver; (B) muscles; (C) brain; (D) nutrition; (E) endurance.

4. Significant changes produced in the body by alcohol are due to: (A) anesthetic effects on the brain; (B) conversion of glucose into an abundance of energy; (C) elevation of brain temperature; (D) all of the foregoing; (E) none of the foregoing.

5. The quality that generally suffers most when the brain is influenced by alcohol is: (A) will power and judgment; (B) emotional maturity; (C) temperature control; (D) diminished glucose metabolism; (E) all of the foregoing.

6. Select the following statement: (A) normal people tend to not repeat negative experiences; (B) there is definite proof that marijuana reduces driving skills; (C) the goal of MADD is to never meet again; (D) in an alcoholic blackout there is no loss of consciousness but there is a loss of memory; (E) all of the foregoing.

7. When an alcoholic becomes sick on consuming a smaller amount of alcohol, the phenomenon is known as: (A) cross tolerance; (B) intolerance; (C) reverse tolerance; (D) tolerance; (E) none of the foregoing.

8. Identify personality changes which frequently occur in the alcoholic: (A) rationalization of drinking; (B) pathologic lying; (C) infantile behavior; (D) denial of illness; (E) all of the foregoing.

Answers1(C); 2(E); 3(C); 4(A); 5(A); 6(E); 7(C); 8(E).

Bibliography

1. David M. Grilley. *Drugs And Human Behavior*. 352 pp. Allyn and Bacon, Boston, Massachusetts, 1989.
2. Charles R. Carrol. *Drugs*. 507 pp. Wm . C. Brown Publishers, Dubuque, Iowa, 1989.
3. Gold, Mark S., M.D. *The Facts About Drugs and Alcohol*. 132pp. Bantam, New York, New York, 1986.
4. Mumey, Jack. *Young Alcoholics*. 198pp. Contemporary Books, Inc., Chicago, Illinois, 1984.
5. Vaughn, Clark. *Addictive Drinking*. 317 pp. Penguin Group, New York, New York, 1982.
6. Milan, James R. and Katherine Ketcham. *Under The Influence*. Bantam, New York, New York, 1981.

Treatment of Alcohol Related Problems

Introduction

Alcohol is the most important and most common drug of addiction. It is one of the most serious problems affecting many more people than just the addicted. There are about 20 million alcoholics in the United States.

Alcoholism ranks behind only heart disease and cancer as a major killer in the United States. The National Council of Alcoholism says alcohol causes deaths from many diverse factors such as accidents, cirrhosis of the liver, seizures, delirium tremens, malnutrition, dementia, suicides and other sources of illness. Suicides alone occur 58 times more often among alcoholics as among nonalcoholics. More than 90 percent of the drugs that are involved in deaths are under legal control or available in over-the counter preparations. Fewer than 10 percent of drug deaths are related to illegally obtained substances. There are many other diseases associated with alcoholism.

The safe comfortable image that all alcoholics are skid row bums has little validity. Derelicts represent only about 3 percent of the nation's alcoholics, according to the National Institute of Mental Health. The vast majority of alcoholics are disseminated throughout society, and can be difficult to identify.

Intervention

Intervention is a type of confrontation that often works to snap users back into reality long enough to show them that their world has turned upside down. Coworkers, bosses, and family members usually confront the alcoholic's behavior based on specific incidences, *guided by a professional interventionist*. This approach is appropriate when individuals have tried unsuccessfully to help a person with a drug problem. A decision to seek help may also be created by the loss of a job, loved ones, or finances, which creates a sense of perspective about what is really important. Any time a professional confrontation is conducted, the family risks alienation of the alcoholic. It's easier to blame another person for problem drinking than to accept the responsibility for one's own behavior.

_____ QUOTATION_____

"Not all fights are bad, in fact they are preferable to disciplined serenity."

William Atwood

The Alcoholic in Industry

The first thing that the interventionist should accept, in attempting to help the alcoholic recognize the problem, is that the interview with the employee will be unpleasant, and that there is never a "right" time to discuss excessive drinking with an alcoholic employee. The supervisor can expect denials, excuses, rage, remorse, lies, and promises. The interventionist must learn not to let himself be put off or diverted. Do not get involved in a discussion of a person's "right" to drink. An alcoholic will attempt to defocus the intervention, to evade the real issue. The person confronting the alcoholic must try to answer in advance all the excuses and tricks that will be used to avoid facing the problem.

The real issue, and nothing else, is that the employee's drinking is causing problems—not spousal problems, difficulties in raising children, finances, or anything else. It is drinking that is responsible for carelessness on the job, poor attendance, poor work performance, and the demoralization of people around the employee.

_____ QUOTATION_____

"The alcoholic presents a painful picture; painful because of the hardship and privations visited upon innocent families; painful because these people, debilitated in mind and body, are incapacitated, unable to carry out the normal routine of their job safely and efficiently".

John Walsh, M.D.

Denial, A Refusal to Believe or Accept

Denial involves an elaborate system of defenses that are used in spite of the consequences of one's actions. It is a protective and defensive mechanism that warps the way the alcoholic sees the world. It is the glue that holds self-esteem together.

44

Time in recovery can erase enough pain to permit the following thoughts, "It wasn't that bad," or "I don't have a problem anymore." Anyone on a diet knows that they will have to watch their weight constantly. Lost weight all too often reappears. All addictions involve problems of "appetite" control.

It is time to take a look at denial, what it might mean, and what it doesn't mean. The standard response in the field of addictions states that belief contradictions or self-denial are part of the disease. Denials may occur in a multitude of ways, such as:

1. Not accepting the evidence that the individual is dependent, regardless of the underlying reasons such as immaturity, willful misconduct, or other causes.
2. Not recognizing or minimizing the amount of chemicals used, the amount of control maintained, or the consequences of drug use.
3. Not accepting the "fact" that the individual has a disease.
4. Not having an acceptable opinion related to drugs, to people who use them or a simple lack of awareness.

Denial, What it Isn't

1. With alcoholics, the benefit of drinking is a short term gain followed by a long term punishment. A decision is made to drink, accepting or taking responsibility for the decision. Often, drugs will be prescribed for legitimate disorders. For example, an endodontist performs root canal surgery, prescribing ten tablets of codeine. The non-narcotic analgesic Motrin (600 mg's) should work perfectly, but the patient decides the narcotic will provide a free high.

It also happens all the time with all kinds of substances. Making a decision to use an illegal drug is not denial. Making a decision to drink if the person has accepted their alcoholism is not denial. After one alcoholic admitted drinking again after a period of sobriety, an inappropriate comment was stated by the discussion leader. "Looks like you forgot the first step." The first step of AA states, "We admitted we were powerless over alcohol and that our lives had become unmanageable." The young man responded, "No, I just wanted to get drunk."

2. People often don't tell the truth, particularly when they believe that doing so would result in unacceptable punishment.

An amateur athlete has been using steroids. His coach asks him if he is using them. The athlete knows the answer is "Yes," but he says, "No". He is clearly not in denial.

45

3. Some drug experts believe in the importance of their treatment philosophy and disagree with the type of help being provided by another team member. Psychological concepts are abused when used as weapons. Denial is used as if it were synonymous with disagreement. How can it be distinguished from lying, disagreeing, or freely making a decision?

Some alcoholics certainly are oblivious to the reality of their addiction but with the passage of time will become aware of their alcohol related difficulties. Perhaps it's a form of self-denial. An alcoholic may think everyone is being fooled. Such is not the case. In reality, an alcoholics are not fooling themselves either.

The Deadly D's

1. Denial. Denial feelings include hostility, being argumentative, rationalization, lying, fear and guilt. Alcoholic turn their eyes away from the problem.
2. Delay. Acknowledgement of a problem but postponement of doing something about it. "Not yet" is a common response.
3. Detour. The drinker puts conditions on sobriety, "Yes, I know but." This person is inwardly angry and defiant. On the surface early sobriety seems a breeze. Frequently, the alcoholic is doing it for someone else.
4. Dilemma. The person is confused, has difficulty in accepting the disease concept and will ask questions such as, "why me?"
5. Defeat. The person is feeling beat or exhausted and says, "I can't drink," but mentally is still being controlled by the drug. There is no commitment to change. The alcoholic is not acknowledging the problem.
6. Dry or Die. The alcoholic believes, "I can't drink but I can't live without it." There is no way out. It's painful.

Problem Solving

You are the wife of a physician who has an active practice. Your husband recently was appointed Chief of Surgery at the hospital, a position confirmed by the Board of Directors. He is respected by his peers and has a very busy, successful medical practice.

On the weekends, when your husband is not on call, he drinks heavily and becomes moody. He almost always drinks at home. Your relationship has suffered over the past four or five years. You find it difficult to respect and love your husband when he drinks. You suspect he is also taking some kind of medication because you have found different types of pills in his pockets when doing the wash. He does not seem interested in the children, his hobbies, or you. On a few occasions he has taken Morphine Sulfate before going into the office, usually after a hectic night of emergency calls. He says the morphine helps steady his hands and take care of the fatigue.

When you have brought up the subject of his alcohol and drug use, he immediately feels criticized and becomes defensive. Frequently he will drink heavily after these conversations and you have become reluctant to discuss this topic with him. What can you do?

_____ QUOTATION _____

Lying to ourselves is more deeply ingrained than lying to others.
Feodoe Dostoevsky

Please make a mental response to any of the following statements you agree with.

1. I would separate from him and consider divorce if he doesn't do something about his life.
2. I would talk to my closest friends and seek advice.
3. I would inform his professional associates, trusting their judgment.
4. I would insist that he contact the employee assistance program (EAP).
5. I would wait until he lost control because he would scare himself, then I would discuss his problem.
6. I would have to overlook his behavior because of his position in the community.
7. I would attend Alanon but not say who I am.
8. I would have our two teenage children talk to him about his drinking problem.
9. I would suggest he take a leave of absence and admit himself into a residential treatment center.
10. I would try to overlook his behavior as our home and family are more important. He should work less.
11. Other? Select the possible solutions you think best.

Criteria to Determine Outpatient versus Inpatient Care

The following factors are influential in making a decision about professional treatment.

1. Money. Much of the Black community, like the Latin and Native American communities have a disproportionate number of people below the poverty level. Their immediate needs are in the areas of

food, adequate housing, health care, and employment. These immediate needs must be considered in any treatment program. The poor do not have money and do not have the same employment opportunities of the more affluent. In the middle class white population, addictive disease is considered a health problem while in lower class minorities it's looked upon as a criminal problem.

2. Number of supporters. If you have any, consider yourself fortunate. *Is the spouse supportive of treatment? Is the spouse an asset?* Women typically underuse treatment services because of the housewife-mother role. Considering the spouse is the husband, would he take care of the children while their mother is undergoing treatment? Another obstacle for the single woman with children, there are very few residential treatment programs which will accept both the mother and her children. In this case, the family is not split up. Another support issue, *are the family members who are sober and involved in the patient's life in a supportive way?* Unfinished family or other conflicts will sabotage a lot of early sobriety. *Finally, does the patient have supporters among friends who are sober?*

3. Employment. *Is the patient still employed? What is the level of drug use on the job?* It is fairly common knowledge that some interstate truck drivers will use amphetamines to keep themselves awake. A bartender may or may not drink. If that bartender is an alcoholic and a neophyte to recovery, the environment is quite conducive to relapse. There's no way an average person can work 80 hours a week without taking a little something extra. The patient's job may threaten outpatient care.

4. *How much physical deterioration has the patient experienced?* If there are a lot of medical problems, patients belong in a hospital. If physical problems are minimal, outpatient services may be sufficient. Many alcoholics are coming in earlier and haven't gone through a total disintegration. Most younger alcoholics use an assortment of drugs, which produces a synergism of negative effects. Cocaine addicts could go directly to outpatient care as there is usually not any immediate medical threat to health.

5. *What's the patient's level of motivation for treatment?* No one is a mind reader. Women, in comparison to men, have lower self-esteem; are less valued in the workplace; get less support for seeking treatment; are more likely to be divorced; conceal their problems longer; are more apt to misuse prescription drugs; and exhibit more feelings of shame, fear, and guilt when they enter treatment. In short, there are more obstacles for women to open up and begin recovery.

Patients say many things about their desire to begin the recovery process, especially when they are suffering. As the pain diminishes, all too often the motivation for recovery lessens. Patients must participate in their own recovery. Unfortunately, memories of the difficulties are minimized and self-will surfaces. Too many will do exactly as they want. Self-will runs riot, and the patient ends up drunk. It is critical for the patients to see themselves as they are, and to determine what they would like to be.

Alcoholics Anonymous

For those alcoholics who have limited funds or other hesitations about entering into a rehabilitation program, here's a little tip. Most rehabilitation programs encourage their patients to participate in Alcoholics Anonymous. This organization exists because alcoholics need help and AA is more successful than psychiatry, the clergy, hospitals or jails in providing that needed aid. The organization works one day at a time for anyone who thinks that help is needed. Membership is anonymous unless the member desires to drop the anonymity.

Alcoholism is one of our country's major public health problems, ranking behind only heart disease and cancer as a killer in the United States. Broken homes, suicide, sickness and other consequences are a result of alcoholism. Basically the alcoholic is the same as any other person with problems and tensions. The alcoholic seeks escape in alcohol. Drinking becomes compulsive. Sooner or later the alcohol will become number one. One drink is too much and a thousand is not enough. The alcoholic has a mental obsession, drinking.

Patterns of drinking in alcoholism are not identical. Some drink daily, some are periodic, some in sprees, some in social groups, some in solitary preoccupation. Social standing is not significant. An alcoholic is a person whose life becomes unmanageable because of alcohol. Domestic or home life and social relationships are disturbed.

Treatment of alcoholism is complex. Stopping drinking seems simple. You just don't drink. The problem is that we see a lot of failures. But many of those who drink again will eventually stop drinking. The physician may help identify the problem but is best at tending to physical problems (pancreatitis, gastritis and ulcers, liver problems, nutritional deficiencies, accidental injury, etc.) The alcoholic is not a desirable patient in most medical offices. Rejection of prescribed treatment, dishonesty, evasiveness, and rationalization of drinking are typical. Alcoholism is best treated by the specialist, a fellow recovering alcoholic, where there is no barrier of misunderstanding. Fears, guilts and self-condemnation and other psychiatric problems are minimized in this relationship.

The first 90 days of membership in Alcoholics Anonymous are most critical. Getting to the first meeting is difficult. Continuing to participate in your own recovery is also difficult. There are erroneously preconceived attitudes that can form barriers to recovery. Force yourself to be open minded. The other members are getting better. If you listen, you will learn even without a thorough understanding.

Help from another alcoholic is something that can be depended on. This is assistance that the problem drinker can understand and have confidence in. The only requirement for membership is a desire to stop drinking. The drinker is accepted without question into the AA group. It is a program of attraction rather than promotion. The 12 Steps of Alcoholics Anonymous constitute a recovery program which begins with the admission that the member is powerless over alcohol and that strength is needed from another source to overcome the problem. A searching, fearless moral inventory of oneself is also part of the program. Restitution to those persons harmed gives emotional strength to the alcoholic. Knowing there is help if a person wants to stop drinking can be vital.

Alcoholics Anonymous was founded by two prominent men whose lives had been seriously affected by excessive drinking. They set out simply to survive. What they did was to try anything and everything, keeping what works and rejecting the rest. AA is at the basis of all good treatment simply because it is the most powerful, and because it is the most scientific of all therapies.

There are no rules, no dues, and participation is voluntary. It is a fellowship based upon a common problem. Sponsors in the organization are available to give support to the newcomer. Suggestions on how to stay sober are exchanged between members. "Tomorrow may never come, yesterday is a cancelled check". The alcoholic can't be cured, but is only an arrested case. If the alcoholic takes a drink again, the problem will surface and the member will be right back in the depths of active alcoholism. The objective is to stay sober today. Alcoholics understand this, simple as it is. Personality reorientation can come later.

The Pepsi Generation

The new generation of alcoholics probably has used cocaine, crystal meth and marijuana. The younger alcoholic has become street wise rapidly, often having broad experiences with a variety of drugs. The greater the diversification of drug experiences, the quicker the "bottom" is reached.

The battle for control over the use of the drug seems to be more dominant in the cocaine abuser, while alcoholics more universally deny their addiction. The more complete denial is observed among alcoholics resulted from the fact that they had struggled with their addiction for longer periods of time (often 10 years or more) punctuated by numerous failed attempts to control their use. Once their denial was broken, however, alcoholics accepted their alcoholism.

The cocaine abusers' average length of addiction was shorter (approximately two years), with fewer abortive attempts to control their use. The shorter duration of addiction allowed them to indulge in fantasies of dealing but not using cocaine, snorting cocaine but not smoking free base, using only for specific periods of time, and deriving all the pleasure without any of the addictive struggle.

One generation is more defiant and street wise, the other more controlling and established. Everybody comes to AA for the same reason. The message is clear, *"Please don't withhold your experience, because you disapprove of the way we got here."* Youth shows its wisdom.

―――――――――――――― QUOTATION ――――――――――――――

"I never suspected that I would have to learn how to live—that there were specific disciplines and ways for seeing the world I had to master before I could awaken to a simple happy, uncomplicated life."

Dan Millman

Growth, A Day At A Time

A recovering alcoholic can become overwhelmed by the eternity of personal growth that comes with recovery. Sometimes the AA member would just like to dump the whole idea of recovery and backslide into old, comfortably painful patterns. Sometimes too, we wonder why we can't ever be finished and just stop for awhile.

Feeling this way can mean it is time to stop and rest. The process of recovery has plateaus and detours along the way, and it's okay at times to take a break. But the "it's too much trouble" feeling also can be a signal that we need to pay more, not less, attention to ourselves and our recovery program.

Just as the chemically dependent person chooses not to drink or use drugs on a daily basis, so must a codependent person choose to continue recovery one day at a time. It is easy to see progress or lack of it in the big choices—to abstain from chemicals, to dissolve destructive relationships, to change careers. Less visible, but at least as important, are the little choices we all make every day.

READING

If Only I Had Paid Attention

Most of what I really needed to know about how to live, what to do, and how to be, I learned in childhood. I learned attitudes and values from my parents and friends.

51

The lessons I learned then are still coming true today. The seeds that were planted are still growing. These are the things I learned: Play fair. Don't hit people. Put things back where you found them. Don't write on the walls. Clean up your own mess. Don't take things that aren't yours. Say you are sorry when you hurt somebody. Stop lighting firecrackers. Wash your hands before you eat. Balance life by learning and playing. Think and work everyday. Take a nap in the afternoon. When you go out into the world, watch out for each other, hold hands and stick together. Be aware of wonder.[1]

Recovery means choosing to confront small instances of abusive behavior instead of letting them go. It means choosing to set boundaries to protect your time for recreation and rejuvenation. It means saying "no" to demands you can't meet. It means deciding every day to take care of yourself by paying attention to your needs for sleep, exercise, and healthy diet.

We can let all these choices overwhelm us if we focus on the "every single day for the whole rest of my life" aspect of them. Or we can take them one day at a time, recognizing that some days are easier than others. And we can remember that, as choosing growth becomes a pattern, it gets easier. Each seemingly insignificant daily choice is a separate affirmation that recovery is worth the trouble.

The cessation of drinking is evidence of success in treatment, but it should not be regarded as the only goal. A more total personality readjustment is desirable. The personal health of the alcoholic, the stability of family life, the ability to hold a job and social adjustment in general should all be considered in judging the rehabilitation value of treatment.

The Relapse Phenomenon

One fact that must be understood about addictive diseases is the phenomenon of relapse either using the primary drug of choice by itself or some other chemical or combination of mind altering substances. From a sheer physical point of view, it appears quite straightforward, the solution obvious. *A psychological analysis of individual thoughts and feelings reveal an extremely complex interaction of mental processes which may well deter one from re-entering the recovery process.* Ironically, the longer a person has been recovering from the disease the more devastating the relapse. On the surface, the person who has been sober for five to fifteen years would appear to have learned the basic skills for living and therefore have an easier time getting sober. Such may not be the case.

"Slip" or relapse is a path returning the user to the misery that brought them to the doors of A.A. or an affiliate program. Nobody ever walked through those doors because it was a good idea. Relapse is a progressive return to impaired behavior, such as chemical dependency, codependency, eating disorders, gambling, and so forth. Relapse is an observable set of symptoms that indicate unhappiness, stress, anxiety, hopelessness and depression, all culminating in a highly probable return to addictive disease or destructive behavior. Both relapse and transfer of addiction may arise from the fact that repeated admissions may be a treatment failure, not client failure.

Prescription Medication and the Recovering Alcoholic

Predisposed individuals are not necessarily protected from drugs with lower re-addiction potential, generally those which seemingly are less potent. Tranquilizers may provide the catalyst to re-awaken the disease, yet in many individuals they may be taken safely under medical direction. The benefits of any psychoactive drug must outweigh the potential risk. A decision of this magnitude must be made by a knowledgeable physician. Some people, often with a family history of addictive disease, are more likely to be hypersensitive to all psychoactive substances. High or low potential risk does not confine itself to drugs alone. Some alcoholics are prone to work addictions, often attempting to make up for lost time. Exhaustion often can lead to relapse. Yet, some medications can be taken with minimal potential risk. For example, Lithium Carbonate is chemically related to sodium and potassium, and will help some patients for depression or mania without risking awakening the addiction.

A physician had been prescribing Dilantin and phenobarbital (a long acting barbiturate) for years due to a seizure disorder in a sober, recovering alcoholic. The young man had no difficulties with his disease of alcoholism. However, he exhibited an immediate compulsion for Seconal (secobarbital) when this medication was prescribed for insomnia related to stress. He was soon taking five to ten capsules a day, which resulted in the death of two people in an automobile accident. After he was detoxified from Seconal, the Dilantin and phenobarbital did not spark any further compulsion. He was not convicted of vehicular homicide.

Using alcoholism as an example: a relapse describes, 1) The return to drinking; 2) The return to periodic bouts of drinking; or 3) behaving like a drunk without having had a drink. The denial, isolation, rage and anger will all affect interpersonal relationships at home and work. If it is not sobriety, it is not recovery.

Resentments Hurt

Resentment can be a motivator, sometimes. It provides the power that pushes you through a barrier, to become superhuman, to prove yourself. However, resentment hurts the one who feels it. This form of anger causes all sorts of emotional problems, from feeling down to outright distress. One thing about resentments, they never hurt the person being resented. When a person has been wronged, hours spent planning the perpetrator's demise is a waste, as paradoxically, the prey is sleeping soundly. Resentments provide rent free space inside your mind to others, frequently contributing to the relapse phenomenon. *Resentments are emotional malignancies.*

You can decide to deal with the resentments and get on with life. It's not necessary to be harmed emotionally because of someone else. The first and most obvious answer is the least tried. Go directly to the person and announce you feel wronged. Look them in the eye, be assertive. Dealing directly with them may be anxiety producing. You may fear the confrontation won't do any good or might damage your relationship with your boss. This stops many people.

Or, try this one. Write down their name and what they did to you, or you fear they will do to you, and then take a good look at what you have written, and ask yourself these things: Is it real? What did their actions threaten in me? Do I have to pay attention to this? And then, throw the paper away and tell yourself the whole mess is now gone from your consciousness.

Sometimes, these techniques place people back on the positive track, instead of rubbing their hands together in negativeness. It may take a few years or disasters to realize it, but the one who holds the pent-up anger is always the one who pays for getting wronged. It is our life and we all have choices, every minute, every hour. Permit your intellect to determine which emotion influences your best interests.

The Long Walk Back—I

The initial thrill of sobriety is a unique experience. Active addiction is in dramatic contrast to the newly experienced sense of physical and mental well-being, with a clarity of mind and the feelings of triumph and dignity. This contrast results in the euphoria of newly found sobriety.

An anonymous physician of the Scripps Clinic and Research Foundation of La Jolla, California, says that the organization of Alcoholics Anonymous knows more about the problems of alcoholism than any other specialized group. *When help is needed, the specialist should be sought.* The cure rate for alcoholics is zero, because, say Doctor George O., alcoholism is a permanent disability. However, 35 percent of those who have been members of AA for less than a year will not pick up another drink. Of those members who have remained sober for 5 years, 80 percent will never drink again.

By reversing the aforementioned figures, about 65 percent of those in early sobriety and about 20 percent with 5 or more years of recovery *will* drink again. Alcoholism is a relapsing illness. Relapse does not prevent reentering recovery. But the alcoholic who has resumed drinking will find it difficult to come back in contact with sober AA members and be truthful. *False pride is a killer.* Seemingly, it would be simple to take a night off and just get drunk. Who would know the difference? You show up at the meeting with that little secret. You don't share it. It's so easy. You could do it again. So begins active relapse.

Sobriety is achieved one day at a time. A recovering alcoholic needs to work diligently on his or her continuing sobriety. The newcomer has devoted a significant portion of life to drinking. The greatest chance for relapse occurs within the first year of recovery. Maybe a new bottom has to be reached. A bottom is primarily a psychological space, many people being outwardly successful and inwardly dead. Think of an elevator ride, the occupant can get off on any floor or proceed to the basement. When the elevator doors open, the ride is over and the passenger walks out into sobriety.

During the early years, sponsorship usually is beneficial. Working the 12 steps will keep you sober and working the traditions will keep the group together and functional. Devote all the time you can to recovering physically, mentally, emotionally and spiritually. Honesty, openmindedness, and willingness to go to any lengths will speed recovery. The twelve step programs are a process that continues throughout life. A recovering alcoholic should be concerned about sobriety 5–10 years after last taking a drink.

Recovery After Relapse

The person who reenters recovery after a relapse may be anticipating the same feeling of exhilaration. But, there is only one first kiss. That initial thrill of sobriety felt the first time around is not there. Even if this alcoholic overcomes those feelings of guilt, failure and embarrassment, there's no way one can reexperience that initial excitement of sobriety, which plays no small part in providing the momentum of early recovery.

A second difficulty regularly encountered by people who have relapsed after years of sobriety is the difficulty in finding another alcoholic who has experienced the same problems. The newcomer has a large number of people from which to get help. Everyone in recovery was at one time a newcomer, and everyone experienced more or less of the struggles of early recovery. Not so with the recovering relapser. This person needs the wisdom and guidance of someone who had relapsed after a long period of sobriety, and was successful at achieving a stable sobriety the second time around. While these people do exist, their numbers are far less than the pool of talent available for the newcomer. In smaller communities it may be especially difficult for the relapser to find someone who shares the experiences.

There are some erroneous attitudes about relapse, such as that the relapser must go back to square one, as if all those years of sobriety were wasted. If a doctor were to prescribe a treatment and the patient didn't respond as was desired, it is doubtful if the physician would turn the patient away. To the contrary, a different series of treatments would be tried. Eventually the patient may respond to an alteration of the treatment plan. Responses vary, skill levels of counselors differ, the patient may be open to new ideas or may shut them out. Is the patient ready to listen and will this person in early recovery be able to put these new suggestions into action? Don't give up. If there is no response, then get resourceful. For example, when a physician treats a patient for any disease and the patient doesn't get better, the mode of treatment is changed until the desired health benefit is obtained. By contrast, when the person being treated for chemical dependency has difficulty maintaining abstinence, he or she is considered to be unmotivated and not ready to recover. In reality the individual may need a change from the traditional treatment to a regimen tailored to his or her own biochemical and behavioral uniqueness.

Minnesota VS Dallas

Some years back I sat in Met Stadium in Minneapolis, MN. A playoff game between the Vikings and Dallas was about to start. It was a cold late December afternoon.

I used reasonable caution walking across the snow-and ice-covered lot, but in spite of this, I slipped and fell numerous times. As upset as I was by the repeated falls, it was obvious that I could not remain lying in the parking lot. I got to my feet and continued to my destination. Despite the frustration of the falls, there was no denying that I was getting closer to the stadium than I had been at the outset. The falls did not erase the progress I had made. Because I continued on towards my goal, my rewards were waiting for me. The game was outstanding.

My picture made the cover of Sports Illustrated Magazine. The 1975 version of a "miracle catch" occurred right in front of me. It was a controversial call, the decision going to Dallas. Their receiver pushed the Minnesota defender, thus gathering in the ball and scoring a touchdown. The

Vikings were out of the playoffs. A Sports Illustrated photographer caught the action on film. In the crowd scene was a big orange dot, a brightly colored snow mobile suit. That was me. Along with 10,000 other fans, we made the cover together.

The Long Walk Back—II

Thus several years of sobriety are not to be dismissed as having been in vain. There is some growth with every day, and the person who reenters recovery comes in as a student with advanced standing, not as a first grader. Denial of this leads to a mistaken assessment of the needs of the person in recovery.

Fools seldom learn from experience. Only the wise learn readily. My increased care and alertness to detect potentially dangerous slippery spots in the parking lot got me back to the car without mishap. Had I not fallen in the first place, it is possible that a later slip could have been one that caused a more serious injury.

Temporary Addictions

There are some involvements, that although they bear some of the marks of addiction, are sometimes said to offer pathways away from addiction. The clearest examples are found among members of alcohol and drug treatment groups. Their commitment to such groups fulfills the criteria for addiction, but members view it as the best way to eliminate a particular unhealthy habit. Often these organizations 1) limit a person's serious contacts to those who share common problems and approach to dealing with them; 2) teach a way of thinking that eliminates doubt and alternate conceptions; 3) provide a group identity and emotional support; 4) encourage regular attendance at meetings and conformity to the suggested steps of recovery; 5) pervade the person's life and protect and cushion the individual.

The program was developed to return people to society as fully functioning members. Alcoholics Anonymous is an ambulatory program. Use it freely. Attend favorite meetings, keep in contact, but go ahead and fulfill your sober destiny. Life will be pleasantly surprising and rewarding. Too many people have taken all kinds of risks when drinking, yet once settled into the nest of AA are reluctant to make productive life changes outside of not drinking or using. Alcoholics Anonymous can become addictive. Your goal is to obtain stability and discover who you are. Being a recovering person means that you have the confidence to take flights away from the nest. AA will provide its members with a philosophy which can be used immediately, the rewards occurring daily. Find a way to get yourself rehabilitated and move on. Embrace life! But, come back to your old friends and visit. The group birthed you, for a second time.

Two additional aspects of involvement with such organizations must be evaluated. The first consideration is whether the negative impact of limiting a person's choices is outweighed by the beneficial impact of ceasing to use drugs or alcohol. The second factor to be weighed is whether the control such groups have over an individual's life is temporary and that the influences are way stations on a path to greater integrity.

The Gamblers's Self-Destructive Drive

It is estimated that there are probably more than one million compulsive gamblers in the United States. Gamblers fit into four broad categories as follows: 1) social; 2) professional; 3) antisocial or 4) compulsive. The social gambler plays for recreation, plays for entertainment and separates it from the rest of his or her life. The professional gambler is in the business to win, is highly disciplined and patient, and accepts losses as a part of the operation. The antisocial gambler cheats, steals and does anything to win. The compulsive gambler is the victim of an uncontrollable preoccupation with gambling that eventually leads to family and social chaos and interference with normal functioning. An irrational optimism about gambling is characteristic and this attitude is generally based on previous big wins and assistance by friends and family during periods of distress.

Large gambling wins during the teenage years often lay the foundation for later compulsive attitudes and beliefs. The compulsive gambler may be highly intelligent, even though emotionally ill, much as the alcoholic and the drug addict. Gamblers often have good memories, keen analytical skills and possibly more intelligence than the average person afflicted with addictive disease.

Treatment is possible. If it were not an addiction, we could simply gain insight into the nature of our behavior and stop it. But we cannot, nor can the alcoholic, compulsive overeater or gambler, or any others who suffer from primary addictive disease. A Twelve Step program for gamblers is Gamblers Anonymous. It is the most successful organization in helping others and the program closely resembles that of Alcoholics Anonymous. Information is available by writing to Gamblers Anonymous National Service Office, Box 17173, Los Angeles, California, 90017.

The Obsessive Personality

Three different patients were compared, all of whom were diagnosed as having obsessive-compulsive personalities, but who were functioning at different levels of competence and adjustment. The three patients, a doctor, a bookkeeper, and a teacher were all basically normal people functioning in society. All these people revealed the same kind of thinking, understanding and reasoning. Inflexibility, mixed attitudes (such as love and hate toward the same person), a ritualistic way of doing things (lining up your canned goods in alphabetical order), the ability to achieve isolation typifies the obsessive-compulsive person.

There are four variables by which different levels of obsession can be distinguished. These are as follows; 1) the capacity to deal effectively with a variety of emotions; 2) the ability to enter into and sustain relationships with others; 3) the ability to be productive in social and work situations, and 4) experiences of a developmental nature that are appropriate to the person's age and which leads to self-respect.

Breaking Obsessive Behavior

Any person trying to stop drinking must know how to break an obsession. Obsessive-compulsive thoughts will occur. It's natural in any recovering alcoholic. Basically an obsession has three main components. If you find yourself becoming determined to drink alcohol or use some other drug, it is an obsession. It must be broken. Sometimes, use of another object can give a momentary relief from the urge, but very soon, the urge returns in full intensity. Everybody will experience awkward, uncomfortable feelings on an irregular basis. The reason people do have addictions is because they have some needs or cravings but are unaware of the nature of these cravings, and because of their lack of understanding them, they try to satisfy them inappropriately.

Nondependent people simply get over awkward emotions, the dependent person will immediately consider "altering these uncomfortable feelings." The alcoholic has a vague sense of something missing, of discontent, but does not know what to do about it. Previous experiences have reinforced the effect that food, alcohol, chemicals or sex have provided relief from certain cravings, and the person mistakenly tries to use these objects to alleviate this other feeling of discontent. The alcoholic thinks. "I can't handle this", or starts blaming people, places and things for their emotional response. Anger may follow. The alcoholic starts thinking how to make these feelings go away. "I'll have a drink!"

In this situation, nothing has actually happened but it's about to. The alcoholic is upset, starts blaming others, plans to alter these feelings, and is going to take a drink. Any substance may provide a very transient kind of relief, but very soon the original unmet craving returns in even greater intensity, since it has been more frustrated than before. Again, this person may try to use one of the inappropriate objects to satisfy the craving. We are seeing the pattern of excesses or addictions developing.

The only action that can break the obsession is to break out of isolation. If the alcoholic is alone, or sometimes with other people, they will drink. It's just a matter of time. An alcoholic in early recovery, will get strong desires to drink, especially when rejected or feeling empty inside. Getting out of isolation means going to an AA meeting, an aftercare group, to your parents, friends, or a sponsor. Ideally a recovering alcoholic needs to be with someone who has experienced similar feeling and was able to deal with them in a way that is not self-destructive. Alcoholics must rediscover self-responsibility, if they are to get well. Recovery is a program of action.

——————— SANTA CLARA COUNTY TRANSIT ———————

"The Way", is painted boldly on the front. "Show Me The Way", covers the entire side of the county bus. If all else fails, buy a day pass. Have faith, the ride may just be worthwhile.

Somewhere in Time

At age 22 she entered a residential treatment center for women and stayed six months . She was discharged after completing treatment and moved into a half-way house for an additional three months. Bonnie had been using heroin, and other drugs, for about seven years. She was not forced into treatment, but volunteered. Emotional pain was the ticket for admission. Her attitude was good and progress was steady.

Once released, she remained clean and sober for eight years and embraced life. Both Narcotics Anonymous and Alcoholics Anonymous provided support, acceptance, friendship and help. Bonnie went to work and became self-supporting. Later she became pregnant and delivered a healthy son. Her life was working. Dreams were becoming true, *she had no significant problem.*

Bonnie decided to go to school. Since this decision would affect her finances, her mother and father accepted their daughter and grandson into the family home. She loved them both. Bonnie continued to work part time and also joined a health spa. She had developed high standards and was definitely a perfectionist. Her weight was close to normal. At school she took a full load, and became an above average student.

Since she was busy with school, work, exercise classes and being a mother, it was quite easy to drop off attendance at N.A. and A.A. meetings. Somewhere in time, Bonnie became bulimic. The more she exercised, the more weight she lost. Bonnie became a vegetarian.

Eventually she hurt her back and the injury required medical treatment. She was prescribed codeine and Valium for her injury. Bonnie had been sober for a long time. She could actually get a little *high* on only three pills. A grain and one-half of codeine! She used to shoot up heroin three or four times a day. Over the months, Bonnie found herself continually running out of pills until she found a doctor who would prescribe a liberal amount of medication. He played games, some sexual, but mostly financial. The doctor would sell anything to the addict. All he required was verification of addictive disease; a safe, steady clientele who would pay in cash. Bonnie patiently waited for the physician to verify her illness. After all she was a pro.

She had a steady prescription, ready to be filled, but she required more. It would be nice to have a reserve, in case she had to go out of town. She wanted to take her son to Disneyland but knew the drugs would run out. She had gone through withdrawal before. The doctor prescribed additional medication. She was happy. There was no trip.

Bonnie's routine was to get up about three in the morning and take eight codeine (4 grains) and 30 mg. of Valium. She could concentrate in the early morning, no one else was up, the drugs helped her function. She usually studied four to five hours. Bonnie was taking about 16, 5 mg.Valium tablets a day (80mg.) and 40 one half-grain tablets of codeine per day (20 grains). A typical day. Clearly, a relapse and transfer of addiction. For the individual with addictive disease controlled use of psychoactive substances becomes very difficult.

Bonnie is being medically detoxified. Her dad dispenses the Valium, a graded reduction minimizes withdrawal complications. The rest is locked up. Her prior doctor is under review for numerous charges involving over twenty patients. She continues her exercise and suffers from an eating disorder. Attendance at self-help meetings is sporadic, she likes to sit up front so no one can see her face. She's doesn't talk because she feels ashamed. The gates to hell are right in front of her. She has a disease that says *she has no significant problem.*

_____ QUOTATION _____

"We all wear masks, and the time comes when we cannot remove them without removing some of our own skin",
                                        Andre Berthiaume

Antabuse

Many drugs have been used on alcoholics in recent years. A considerable amount of publicity has been given to the use of Antabuse. To be effective in the control of drinking, Antabuse must be taken about 12 hours before alcohol is consumed. Under these circumstances the drinking of alcohol brings on a number of distressing symptoms that prompt the person to forego liquor.

The drinker is liable to experience first a feeling of heat in the face followed by an intense flushing of the face and neck. Most patients become nauseated 30 to 60 minutes after drinking alcohol. Flushing of the face disappears and is replaced by pallor and a drop in blood pressure. More alcohol is apt to result in dizziness and unconsciousness.

First of all, Disulfiram (Antabuse) can produce violent vomiting in a patient who consumes alcohol. It is a prescription medication manufactured in two doses, 250 mg. and 500 mg. Antabuse will only work if the patients are willing to consume the medication on their own. Once taken, the alcoholic will not be able to drink alcohol without getting very ill. The smaller dose should be sufficient for a lighter person, the larger dose is for the bigger person. Side effects are minimal, however the physician should make the final decision for each individual patient.

The thinking ability of alcoholics is impaired while drinking and in the first stages of recovery. The purpose of sobriety is to lead to the recovery process. The fact is that most alcoholics have sobered up thousands of times. If it's possible to stretch out the time in sobriety, then the alcoholic has the opportunity to grow and begin recovery. The patient should show evidence of emotional growth. When an alcoholic is newly sober, there will be problems reacting to fears, anxieties, job insecurities, divorce and many more. An alcoholic is especially vulnerable in the first 90 days. The alcoholic thinks differently than the non-alcoholic individual. Recovery takes personal responsibility.

Since drugs do not resolve the emotional problems that many alcoholics have and do not alter the personality of the drinker, no long-term cures can be expected from their use. They must be used in conjunction with other methods of treatment for best results. In short, drugs do not produce a permanent or long-lasting solution to drinking. *Antabuse only buys time for the brain to recover.*

Metabolism of Alcohol

The liver is the primary part of the body that converts alcohol into less harmful substances. More than 90 percent of ingested alcohol is changed into carbon dioxide and water. To achieve this result enzymes of the liver change alcohol into a series of substances, such as aldehydes and acetates. In the adult, the average rate by which alcohol can be changed is about 10 milliliters per hour and no practical way of speeding up this process has been found. The specific action of the anti-alcohol cells of the body are highly technical in name and complicated in action. The abbreviated diagram simplifies the metabolic process.

	*Alcohol
	*Acetaldehyde
Alcohol Dehydrogenase	*Co Enzyme A2
(*an enzyme)	*Acetic Acid
	*CO_2 + H_2O

Alcohol is converted into acetaldehyde, Co Enzyme A2, Acetic Acid, and CO_2 +H_2O. The catalyst, an enzyme identified as Alcohol Dehydrogenase starts the process of metabolizing or oxidation. Antabuse negates the enzyme enabling the acetaldehyde to break down into CoEnzyme A2. Therefore, a person taking Antabuse is unable to break down the acetaldehyde.

As this breakdown product increases, so does the flushing, nausea and vomiting. It's impossible to consume alcohol and antabuse together without getting sick. Many over-the-counter products containing alcohol will also make you sick if they are consumed. Nyquil, Scope, and many cough medicines contain alcohol.

The "Oriental Flush" arises in those who have an ineffective version of a liver enzyme that is crucial to the body's breakdown of alcohol. This less effective enzyme allows the buildup of an alcohol product, acetaldehyde, which is sickening and leads many Asians to shun alcohol. Most Asians will stop drinking when the Oriental "flush" occurs.

Failure to Cope

Coping with a challenge has three aspects, 1) recognizing it; 2) organizing means to meet it, and 3) acting to overcome the disturbance that the challenge has produced.

Success in coping depends on intelligence and experience, but each person has a limit in meeting challenges that cannot be exceeded. People need to cope not only with the unpleasant events of life such as death, examinations, accidents and so on, but highly exciting things such as falling in love, getting married, having a baby, and other events. Thinking at this higher level of arousal is generally a pleasurable experience, but if it continues for too long without a solution to the challenge, an underlying depression may develop.

People who fail to cope with challenges may be divided into three groups, as follows: 1) those who need a protected life as they simply do not have the ability to cope, even with small problems; 2) those who are overwhelmed with a succession of major challenges or stresses, and 3) those persons who have superior abilities, excessive internal drives, or ambitions that result in unendurable work loads.

There are five major signs of coping failures: 1) sleep disturbance; 2) menstrual disturbances in women and impotence in men; 3) infertility in women; 4) weight changes that may involve loss of appetite or compulsive eating, and 5) compulsive behaviors which may involve eating, working, studying, turning to alcohol or other drugs, compulsive sexual behavior and others.

Extensive research has found a number of stress reduction methods to be helpful.

1. Removal to a more peaceful, or less stressful environment.
2. Improvement of the capacity to withstand stress by a gradual increase in exposure to stressors. (After the emotions have begun the healing process.)
3. Use of a skill or determination to face a problem or achieve mastery over the environment.
4. Provisions of examples of well-adapted or normal behaviors.
5. Satisfaction of a biological need, such as hunger, thirst or sex.
6. Meditation.
7. Progressive muscle relaxation.
8. The use of biofeedback techniques in response to body signals that conscious control is needed over certain functions.
9. Retraining through individualized care and guidance that result in "corrective emotional experiences."
10. Psychiatric treatment for counseling and other procedures to blunt damaging experiences.

The amount of unmanageability in life is multiplied by alcohol and drugs. There is a synergism of negative effects on lives, multiplied astronomically. Alcoholism and drug dependency is a progressive, chronic disease which affects about 10 percent of the population.

A person afflicted with addictive disease is dying on the installment plan, so are family members. The alcoholic must change his or her behaviors but cannot do so without help. Assistance usually comes from another recovering alcoholic, out-patient care, in-patient care or counseling.

Addictive Diseases

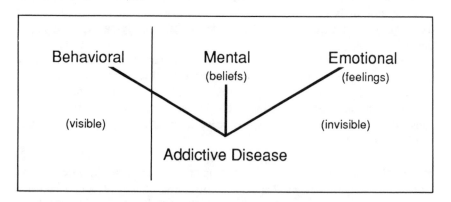

Behavioral. Addictive or compulsive behavior is most visible because it deviates from the norm. All behavior is capable of being seen. Isolation is noticed. One common misconception, once addictive behavior is stopped, is

64

that the person will have licked the problem. Not quite. *The problem is not in the chemical but in the user of the drug.*

The person will become acutely aware of their emotions. The same emotional equipment is still there. Retarded emotional reactions will produce hostilities, frustrations, resentments, and anxieties. People newly sober will be on an emotional roller coaster, prompting some people to say, "I liked you better when you were drinking." Alcoholics in early recovery tend to isolate themselves, even in a room full of people. Silence can kill. An alcoholic who has stopped drinking has not overcome pre-existing problems. Drinking is a symptom of the problem. Sobriety represents a beginning and is a major step to recovery.

Mental. Thoughts and beliefs are often very private. Any person who opens up and shares their thoughts, will reveal a part of their innermost being. Every addicted person has a unique system of thinking. There is a unique combination of denial, rationalization and projection, resulting in a line of thinking that at first sounds logical, but on further analysis is totally absurd.

Invariably the alcoholic will come to the conclusion that taking a drink is the right thing to do at this time. Accept the fact that the alcoholic will continue to see themselves as no good, yet will say, "nothing is wrong with me." The drinker holds onto emotional and mental problems with growth in sobriety. People will say, "there is nothing wrong with my thinking", usually coupled with, "I am no good". Don't overlook that the addict can hold on to contradictory and incompatible ideas simultaneously.

A 22 year old alcohol addict said. "I know it's absolutely impossible for me to stop by myself, maybe." It should not surprise anyone that chemically-dependent people are very sincere, are unaware that much of their thinking is ridden with internal contradictions and inconsistencies. An alcoholic will continue to have basic thinking and emotional problems.

Emotional. Feelings are very personal, and invisible to most people. Most problems have been anesthetized and have never been successfully resolved. The alcoholic has not experienced any substantial emotional growth while drinking. The alcoholic is someone who has not grown emotionally since seeking continual escape into drugs. Problems arise by reacting to original unresolved conflicts or situations for which they are inexperienced. Stopping the act of committing chemical suicide produces other problems. The alcoholics get sober and can't control their feelings and will blame others for their reactions creating a barrier to recovery.

Conflicts have two parts: 1) the idea or concept of the problem and; 2) the feeling associated with the conflict. *The issue is how to live, and deal with conflict.*

65

"The alcoholic has the unique ability to develop a fear of being sober which is greater than living the known consequences of the disease."

Chuck Brissette

An alcoholic who seems to have reached a plateau in recovery, especially if relapse occurs, needs to search carefully for the presence of contradictory thinking. The recovering person has to accept the need for help with thoughts and feelings or they will deny anything is wrong.

The recovering alcoholic is prone to self-deception, and can be honestly dishonest with themselves. If nothing is wrong a new barrier is constructed. Barriers to recovery revolve around overcoming denial. Holding on to emotional and mental problems will stimulate a return to drinking or other undesirable actions and behaviors.

Recovered Or Recovering

Recovery is a process, it's not an event. One of the big fallacies that people have is that they will enter into some kind of treatment such as inpatient, outpatient or see a therapist and they are going to get better and they don't have to think about it again. Recovery is something that a person works on throughout their lifetime. One never recovers, but is always recovering.

Summary

Intervention is a type of confrontation where you can anticipate an alcoholic to defend inadequate work performances with denials, make excuses, rage, be remorseful, lie and make promises. The kind of treatment and care that an alcoholic is likely to receive depends on financial status, family support of a psychological and practical significance, the quality and degree of job relationship, the extent of physical deterioration of the patient and the strength of motivation.

It is often difficult for the problem drinker to attend meetings of Alcoholics Anonymous. The first attendance is especially trying because the alcoholic is apt to be embarrassed, fearful, and ignorant of the kind and quality of reception by the group.

Cessation of drinking is not the only evidence of successful treatment for the alcoholic. Other goals are important, such as adjustments in personality, improved physical health, stability in family life, continued employment and good social adjustment. The sober alcoholic may suffer one or more relapses with a primary or secondary drug. The individual will again suffer from impaired behaviors including stress, anxiety, hopelessness and depression.

When the alcohol addict first experiences sobriety, it is a unique experience. It brings clarity of mind and feelings of triumph and dignity. The highest rate of relapse occurs in the first year of sobriety. The wisdom and guidance of alcoholics who have gone through one or more relapses may be helpful.

The alcoholic is prone to self deception. Recovery is not a cure. It is an interim that must be worked on throughout a lifetime. One never recovers from alcoholism but is always in a state of continued growth.

Self Test

1. Which of the following effects of alcohol is likely to occur first in most people? (A) loss of coordination and balance; (B) loss of consciousness; (C) loss of restraint and judgment; (D) slurring of speech.

2. The two organs that researchers feel are most damaged by prolonged excessive use of alcohol over a period of years are: (A) heart and brain; (B) brain and liver; (C) heart and liver; (D) stomach and liver.

3. The most common reason why the alcoholic uses alcohol is: (A) rejection or loneliness; (B) as an expression of hostility; (C) to produce pleasure: (D) as a substitute for obligations and as an escape from situations which are intolerable.

4. One of the very earliest signs of damage to the brain from drinking is: (A) brain wave changes; (B) temporary loss of memory; (C) development of solitary compulsive drinking habits; (D) attacks of vomiting.

5. Alcoholism is difficult to treat because: (A) the alcoholic does not accept the problem and doesn't really wish to give up alcohol; (B) the cause is difficult to diagnose, making it difficult to cure; (C) alcoholism is a moral problem; (D) alcoholism can't be treated.

6. The goal of treating the alcoholic should be: (A) total and permanent abstinence; (B) prolonged restraint; (C) social drinking with moderation; (D) cross addiction.

7. About what frequency of alcoholism can be expected to occur in the United States population who consumes alcoholic beverages? (A) 1 in 5; (B) 1 in 10; (C) 1 in 20; D) 1 in 50.

8. The fundamental problem of alcohol is: (A) its effect on behavior; (B) its effect on the liver; (C) its relationship to obesity; (D) its relationship to mental illness; (E) its relationship to physical health.

Answer: 1(C);2(B);3(D);4(B);5(A);6(A);7(B);8(A).

Notes

1. Adapted and modified from: Fulghum, Robert. *All I Really Needed to Know I Learned in Kindegarten*. Villard Books, New York, New York, 1986.

Bibliography

1. Robertson, Nan. *Getting Better: Inside AA*. 272 pp. Fawcett Crest, New York, New York, 1988.
2. Wuertzer, Patricia and Lucinda May. *Relax, Recover*. 140 pp. Harper and Row, San Francisco, CA, 1988.
3. Lasater, Lane. *Recovery From Compulsive Behavior*. 128pp. Health Communications, Inc., Deerfield Beach, Flordia, 1988.
4. Mueller M.D., L. Ann and Katherine Ketcham, *Recovering*. 303pp. Bantam Books, New York, New York, 1987.
5. Ray, Oakley. *Drugs, Society and Human Behavior*, 4th Ed. C. V. Mosby, St. Louis, Missouri, 1987.
6. Custer, Robert M.D., and Harry Milt. *When Luck Runs Out: Help for Compulsive Gamblers and Their Families*. 325 pp. Warner Books, New York, New York, 1985.

CHAPTER FOUR

Drug Testing and Interpretation of Results

Introduction

Recently federal agencies have passed drug-free workplace legislation. The new laws establish guidelines and regulations that assist in achieving the national goal of a drug-free society. These guidelines impact all federal workplaces and many private ones that work under government contract.

Supreme Court Upholds Drug Testing Accuracy

With its first decision on drug testing in the workplace, the U.S. Supreme Court not only upheld the Federal Government's right to screen certain employees for illegal drug use but affirmed the technical accuracy and reliability of drug testing and procedures. Employers who follow established guidelines can now focus on the justification for testing workers without worrying about challenges to the accuracy and reliability of test results. The Supreme Court decision affirmed the right of the Federal Government to use justifiable means to secure a drug-free workplace.

Drugs in the Workplace

The National Council of Alcoholism estimates that one employee in 20 has an alcohol or drug problem that affects work performance. Either the employee's own substance abuse or that of a close family member may impair the quality of work.

Alcoholism costs industry billions of dollars a year through work absences, time and material wasted by workers suffering on-the-job-effects of drinking and the cost of training employees to replace discharged alcoholics. Surveys of large companies have indicated that most chief executives were conscious of the general problem, but claimed it wasn't serious in their industry and didn't exist among top management. In the eyes of specialists, that's dangerous self-deception and often a cover up for executive colleagues.

Combating alcohol and drugs in a business is never easy. Supervisors are not qualified to diagnose addiction, and many will not confront an employee on something so personal. But supervisors can see when someone isn't performing and can insist that the person seek help, from company counselors or on the outside. Even elemental responsibility requires staff training and retraining.

Drug Detection Periods

Amphetamine and Methamphetamine: Amphetamine and Methamphetamine are members of a class of central nervous system stimulants whose chemical structure is closely related to several common antihistamines. Currently methamphetamine appears to be more frequently abused compared to amphetamine because of its easy synthesis in illicit laboratories.

Studies have shown that amphetamine and methamphetamine are detectable for two to four days after their use. Because of the structural similarity to some common antihistamines, the commonly used EMIT method which depends upon chemical structure to make a positive identification, cannot differentiate between these drugs. However a combination of the EMIT method with other techniques enables identification of amphetamine and methamphetamine with high specificity.[1]

Barbiturates: Barbiturates are central nervous system depressants. The barbiturate family includes: butalbital, phenobarbital, secobarbital, amobarbital, and pentobarbital.

Within the family, barbiturates are classified as "short to intermediate acting, or long acting." Short to intermediate can be detected two to four days after use while long acting may be detectable for approximately 14 days.

The EMIT method of urinalysis is able to detect the barbiturates as a family. Other tests are able to differentiate the individual barbiturate members.[1]

Benzodiazepines: Benzodiazepines are a closely related family of approximately twenty drugs. They are frequently used as sedatives, hypnotics and antiepileptic agents. Some of the more commonly used benzodiazepines are diazepam (Valium) and chlordiazepoxide (Librium).

Methods developed for urinalysis focus on the benzodiazepine metabolites. EMIT was designed to detect oxazepam (a common metabolite of many benzodiazepines). However it will also help to detect several other closely related benzodiazepines drugs or metabolites.[1]

70

Cocaine: Cocaine is a naturally occurring central nervous system stimulant derived from the leaves of the coca plant. The abuse of cocaine in the United States has dramatically risen since the mid-1970's, and it is considered one to the most highly abused drugs today. Its popularity is due to its extreme rapid onset of action and its ability to generate intense feelings of euphoria. Cocaine metabolites can be detected in the urine for up to two days, however, the popularity of repetitive, frequent use increases detection time.

The EMIT method which detects certain cocaine metabolites is widely used along with other tests.[1]

Marijuana: Marijuana is a plant which produces variable amounts of a psychoactive substance known as THC. Improvements in cultivation methods have gradually increased the potency of this plant. Currently, the amount of THC in a marijuana plant averages four percent. However, concentrations close to nine percent have been attained by a specially cultivated type of marijuana plant called sensemilla.

Many issues have arisen with respect to the interpretation of a positive result. One issue is the long time frame during which the cannabinoids (marijuana metabolites) can be detected. They are detectable weeks to months after cessation. Another issue is the possibility of "passive inhalation." This implies that the subject did not use the drug, but was in close proximity to those who were.

Both of these issues can be overcome with a higher detection level. PharmChem employs the use of EMIT testing, which is capable of higher detection levels. EMIT testing is marketed in two versions. One for the low "passive inhalation" amounts and one for the high, recently injested amounts. The test designed for high amounts is not able to detect the involuntary inhalation of smoke, or detect if someone has not smoked for 10 to 14 days prior. The higher detection level solves many of the interpretation issues.[1]

Methadone: Methadone is used for the treatment of opiate addiction. A daily dose as a replacement for heroin would allow the addict to function normally. It is itself addictive and therapy is aimed at the maintenance of constant usage. Methadone or its metabolite can be detected from 24 to 48 hours after use. Excretion of methadone is highly dependent on the pH of the urine. Thus if it is not detected, it does not mean that a dose has been skipped.[1]

Opiates: The opiates are a group of drugs originally derived from the opium poppy. These drugs are central nervous system depressants whose use provides relief from pain along with a dream-like euphoric state. Continued usage leads to physical addiction. The two major opiates are codeine and morphine. Chemical modifications of these two drugs have produced additional semi-synthetic opiates such as heroin, hydromorphone (Dilaudid), and oxycodone (Percodan).

71

Heroin is usually detectable in a morphine state for two to four days. Codeine is also found for two to four days after use.

Another source of morphine ingestion is the poppy seed. Frequent poppy-seed ingestion is used as a defense for a positive morphine test.[1]

Phencyclidine: Phencyclidine (PCP), is a highly popular drug of abuse. It is legally used as an animal tranquilizer. When injected it can cause sedation, euphoria, confusion, agitation, and combativeness. PCP can be easily produced in illicit laboratories, along with an number of altered forms or "analogs."

PCP is detectable for two to seven days, chronic abuse may result in detectable levels for longer periods of time. Almost all of the analytical methods available are capable of detecting PCP. There is no legal, prescribed, use for PCP for humans.[1]

Alcohol: Ethyl alcohol is probably the most widely used and abused substance. Alcohol is rapidly absorbed into the blood stream, and is distributed rapidly throughout the body. This characteristic differentiates alcohol from other drugs of abuse because of the concentration level in the blood, breath and urine. There is a 1 to 3 ratio of urine alcohol concentration to blood alcohol concentration.

Alcohol is rapidly eliminated. One or two drinks the night before should not produce a positive result. Alcohol can be detected in urine utilizing EMIT and GC methodologies.[1]

Testing:
- Thin Layer Chromatography: TLC
- High Performance TLC: HPTLC
- Gas Chromatography: GC
- Gas Chromatography/Mass Spectrometry: GC/MS
- Enzyme Immunoassay: EMIT

QUESTION

"When should a company institute screening for drug abuse?"

There are three frequently cited reasons that constitute reasonable grounds for conducting drug testing:

1. Public/safety. This is of utmost concern in business where employees are responsible of the well-being of large numbers of people, such as the airlines, railroads and other forms of travel.
2. Employee Safety. Accidents caused from drugs can lead to injuries in the workplace. Failure to remove drugs from the working environment could lead to legal action for liability and negligence.

3. Corporate Reputation. This involves all employees. Failure to produce properly made products can endanger the reputation of the company.

∎

Summary

Multiple methods are now available for the analysis of drugs of abuse. By combining methods, unequivocal identifications are possible. The National Institute on Drug Abuse (NIDA), various State laws concerning methadone patients or corrections personnel and individual employers have all established testing standards depending upon the population to be tested and the objective of the testing.

Self-Test

1. Alcoholic workers cost industry billions of dollars a year because of: (A) work absences; (B) wasted time on the job; (C) materials destroyed by carelessness; (D) costs of training new employees; (E) all of the foregoing.

2. Valium is a commonly used: (A) amphetamine; (B) barbiturate; (C) benzodiazepine; (D) methamphetamine; (E) none of the foregoing.

3. The Supreme Court has ruled that: (A) employees can be screened for drug abuse; (B) industry has no right to test workers for use of drugs; (C) drug testing is a violation of individuals freedom; (D) intoxicated employees can be discharged without further investigation; (E) none of the foregoing.

4. The maximum period of time during which marijuana can be detected after cessation of its use is: (A) three days; (B) ten days; (C) three weeks; (D) one or two months; (E) about two years.

5. Two major opiate drugs commonly used in the United States are: (A) marijuana and morphine; (B) codeine and morphine; (C) marijuana and codeine; (D) alcohol and marijuana; (E) heroin and alcohol.

6. EMIT is: (A) a code for identification of cocaine; (B) a laboratory procedure for detection of benzodiazepine metabolites; (C) a code for the presence of morphine in the blood; (D) a testing procedure restricted to discovery of drug residues in the urine; (E) educational materials for instruction of management.

7. Phencyclidine is legal for use: (A) as an animal tranquilizer; (B) in all human emergencies; (C) in case of shock only; (D) as a stimulant; (E) when prescribed for humans by veterinarians.

8. When should a company institute screening for drug abuse? (A) in business where employees are responsible of the well-being of large

numbers of people; (B) for employee safety, accidents caused from drugs can lead to injuries in the workplace; (C) failure to produce properly made products; (D) all of the foregoing; (E) none of the foregoing.

Answers: 1(E); 2(C); 3(A); 4(D); 5(B); 6(B); 7(A); 8(D).

Notes

1. "Reprinted from the PharmChem Newsletter c. 1989, PharChem Laboratories, Inc., by permission."

Alcohol and the Family

Introduction

Research shows that one out of three children enrolled in school systems in the United States has a chemically-dependent parent. This same research also demonstrates that these young people are at a higher risk of developing a harmful dependency to alcohol or other drugs than other children from non-chemical abusing families. Children from chemically-dependent families, generally, have been untreated, misdiagnosed, or ignored altogether.

The Texas Commission on Alcoholism and Drug Abuse selected 18 Children of Substance Abusers Programs and funded them statewide. These programs are designed to assist children and adolescents, and other significant family members. Their goal is help develop positive coping mechanisms, to increase self-concepts, and to aid in understanding chemical dependency as a disease. The emphasis is on five essential messages for Children of Substances Abusers: (1) It's not their fault a family member is chemically dependent; (2) They can't cure that family member; (3) As a member of the family, they need help themselves; (4) Chemical dependency is an illness; and (5) Recovery is possible; dependents can and do get better.

ANECDOTE

To Never Know Dad

"Dad, I hope you are doing better. The main reason I'm writing you this letter is to thank you for all the great things you have done for me. Just to name a few that will stay clear in my mind forever is building Dusty's stall and of course giving me the pony. I look back at those unforgettable years and can't even compare them to this past year. It seems like everything has changed, *mainly you.*

When I talked to you on the phone, I felt so confident that you finally got your life back together, but I was wrong. I had so much faith in you, and it really hurt me to hear you began drinking or whatever it might be all over again.

Dad, you have so much going for you. Personality, intelligence and your unique sense of humor. It hurts me to see your life taken over by alcohol and cocaine. You might be thinking that I really don't care that much about you. But you're completely wrong. I think about you everyday. I want the "DAD" I once knew.

I love you dearly and will remember how well you raised me from the time I can remember. Dad, I have faith in you and know some-time, when the time is right you will realize that you are mentally stronger than "that drug" and from there you can lead a much better life. I know it's very difficult, but I know from the bottom of my heart that you are capable of doing it.

No matter what, I will keep in touch with you because you are a very special part of my life. I want to stress how much you mean to me and to thank you for the great years we had as a family."

I love you.
Kim P.

Children of Alcoholics, A Hidden Tragedy

Experiences with alcoholics and their families verify that the children of the actively drinking alcoholic are the victims in a hidden tragedy.

In efforts to rehabilitate the alcoholic, the family tends to be totally ig-nored and children are apt to remain invisible. Contemporary alcohol and drug treatment programs generally provide the opportunity to family mem-bers for counseling. All family members go through the enabling process to some degree. Enabling is covering up for the alcoholic and consequences of the drinking. One problem with codependent counseling is the anger the enabler is experiencing. The family member may choose not to participate in this aspect of the treatment program. The pain of living in a world of al-coholism will persist. The co-dependent often is not especially supportive of the alcoholic. The hurt slices too deep. The family may not be an asset for the recovering alcoholic. The chances for relapse increase if an alcoholic returns home to be confronted with unfinished business. It may be in everybody's best interest if the newly-sober alcoholic does not return home immediately after discharge. The hope and trust of the child can shatter if the parent stops drinking and then relapses. The dreams of regaining a "normal" parent are crushed again. The family of the alcoholic also needs attention. The alcoholic gets all the attention, and represents only half the problem.

The enabler, a close family member, desperately tries to cover up the problem, insisting everything is okay. Small children learn to distrust and ignore what they know to be true. Most children feel anger toward their parents. Knowing such feelings were "bad," the anger is turned inward, blaming themselves. Spontaneous, expressive impulses die, and the child becomes like a small, serious grown up, stifling feelings. Children don't want to spill the family's darkest secret after years of telling teachers, employers, and friends that everything is fine. They would get punished if they said otherwise. The child is forced to assume many of the adult responsibilities, because of family dysfunction. There is one main priority, survival.

The child in the home of the alcoholic is apt to feel unloved and neglected. As one child said, "My parents make you feel like a burden." It is understandable that the alcoholic in an uncomfortable, and guilt-ridden condition may be unable to establish a loving and meaningful relationship with his or her child. We are all children until our parents die. Alcoholics see the world through a fog that cannot be penetrated by the emotions of the people around them, even if they are trying to reach out and help. In this condition the alcoholic will become isolated and become unable to reach out and relate to others, even his or her own children. The other parent, who is not an alcoholic, may be overcome with anger, frustration, and futility to such an extent that the normal amount of love and attention is not forthcoming for the child. Some wives showed a lack of insight or anxiety about their drinking husbands, or had a cold indifference to the problem. The spouses were often evasive and uncooperative, withheld information, and resented any self-examination. About one-half of those living with an alcoholic had varying degrees of emotional problems. More important was the finding that 50 percent of the spouses of the alcoholics had "normal" personalities, but were reacting to the stress of the disease. Spouses can come to resemble drunks, since their anger and fears are enormous, way beyond what you would find in a truly sober person.

Since alcoholics become self-centered and preoccupied with their own problems and the other parent is emotionally upset, there may be little emotional understanding left for the child. If the mother is the alcoholic the situation is even more desperate, especially for young children who are normally more dependent on their mothers.

The child becomes insecure because of inconsistent, erratic, and often violent behavior of the alcoholic parent. A child may be in constant fear of physical violence because of the aggressive behavior of the alcoholic. The child is witness to quarrels of the parents and fears the threats of separation, so that home life provides none of the usual security. The child will get minimal comfort at home for problems experienced outside the house. The home may be no haven. Maybe the child will react to the chaos by trying to keep everything in their life under control, and thus give the impression that everything is fine. The children that live in an alcoholic household never have an environment that is consistent and structured. They have to create their own.

As the child grows older, the erratic behaviors and isolation in their own world set a pattern that the child may follow. Children do not want others to know about domestic problems. A false front is presented to friends, the child lies or builds fantasies about his or her parents and close friendships become difficult to form. Male children of alcoholics often become assertive, rebellious and hostile. Daughters tend to become self-defeating, pessimistic, withdrawn and fluctuating in their moods. In short, both sons and daughters have behavior problems. They typically do not do well in school because they cannot concentrate. The children of alcoholics closely resemble alcoholics. In fact, one in four becomes an alcoholic, as compared with one in 10 out of the general population. They are likely to become alcoholics because drinking helps these children become less rigid, loosen up and relax. For those stuck in unhealthy patterns, alcohol may be the only thing that can provide relief.

Some children sublimate their problems and use school as a tool to increase their self-confidence. Reading and perpetual study can provide a healthy way to escape and receive recognition for their accomplishments. Bibliotherapy can be useful for a time, but the victims must satisfy their overpowering desire and hunger for affection by connecting with other people. Most children complain that life is no fun. Children from alcoholic families will be constantly anxious about how things will be at home when they are away from it. The children grow up watching one out of control person trying to control another, and they don't know what normal is. They may move out, but they never leave their parents behind. Most of what our parents give us is their attitudes and values but in this case the values and attitudes are out of line. What develops is a skewed sense of values.

―――――――――― QUOTATION ――――――――――

Think of addictive disease not as an illness that affects bodily organs but as "an illness that affects families. Perhaps the worst single feature of alcoholism, is that it causes people to be unreasonably angry at the people that they most love."

George Vaillant

In "Adult Children of Alcoholics," Janet Geringer Woititz discusses 13 traits that most children from alcoholic households experience to some degree. These problems can pose lifelong challenges.

Adult Children of Alcoholics . . .

1. guess what normal behavior is.
2. have difficulty following a project from beginning to end.
3. lie when it would be just as easy to tell the truth.
4. judge themselves without mercy.
5. have difficulty having fun.
6. take themselves very seriously.
7. have difficulty with intimate relationships.
8. overreact to changes over which they have no control.
9. constantly seek approval and affirmation.
10. feel that they are different from other people.
11. are super-responsible or super-irresponsible.
12. are extremely loyal, even in the face of evidence that loyalty is undeserved.
13. tend to lock themselves into a course of action without giving consideration to consequences.

ANECDOTE

Family Secrets

"I have locked this family secret so deep within me for so many years that finally when I was able to verbalize it, I feel relieved. Sadness and loss can be dealt with now. All children were affected. One of my brothers and one of my sisters are using alcohol to cope with life's frustrations.

I do not blame my parents for what they have done and I do believe that they did the best they could. I have always known that life was not easy for them either.

As a child I was extremely withdrawn and shy and never caused any problems for my parents. I have repressed all my feelings. It was very lonely when my mother gave me the responsibilities at age nine to care for my two younger brothers and sister and to cook for the family. I was so over-whelmed, my angers were internalized. These resentments surfaced as physical pains and resulted in several abdominal surgeries.

The need to control is because as children we try to bring back sanity. My mother's means of control was being passive-aggressive. After each argument with my father she would cry for several hours and then not speak to my father for several weeks. These feelings of silence were extremely frightening for us children as we did not know whether they would be divorced or would abandon us. We were always confused, and thought we were the cause of the unhappiness. I find myself using silence as a punishment even now. The need to control dominates my life. Lifelong coping methods are so difficult to let go.

It has helped me to know that so many other adult children of alcoholics and drug abusers have experienced a similar childhood. Recognizing this fact is one step toward your own recovery." ACOA

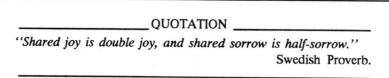

Claudia Black is a nationally recognized authority on the children of alcoholics, as youngsters, adolescents and adults. Several years ago she lectured at the University of Utah where she presented the following steps in the process of recovery.

1. Explore the past, don't be scared to remember
2. However, don't get stuck in the past. You don't want to live in fear.
3. Recovery takes time, it won't happen overnight.
4. Recovery is a process, not an event. You need to be patient.
5. Acknowledge the little things, not everything has to be a major accomplishment.
6. Be willing to give up control, let others help in the situation.
7. Fears are greater than reality. Realize why you have those fears and how to deal with them.
8. It is important to feel and don't bottle feelings up. That does more damage.
9. Your needs are important. Don't be partially satisfied.
10. Set clear limits and know your boundaries.

Children of alcoholics often display a kind of childish loyalty even when it is clearly undeserved. Many of these children have been deprived of their childhood, taking on many adult responsibilities to help make the family work. These children can feel haunted by a sense of failure for not having saved their parent or parents from drink. And as they grow up, they are prone to marry alcoholics or severely troubled people because, for one reason, they're willing to accept unacceptable behavior. They understand the dysfunction of addiction. Children of alcoholics possibly have learned how to cope with the dysfunction. Six year olds run families, and in doing so have been deprived of their own childhood. More commonly, they may hope to be able to influence the situation favorably. This behavior of family members has all the characteristics of addictive behavior. The drugs are "self-denial" and "caretaking." Many have become addicted to domestic turmoil. The only thing that finally stops the relationship is when the pain of continuing characteristic behavior is greater than the pain in giving it up.

In this sense and in several other ways, their often obsessive personalities and tendency to have a poor self-image, closely resemble that of alcoholics. Family members tend to deny their own personal needs. The "mission" of a co-alcoholic is the wish to help others in their need and the determination to give their particular concept of help because of the belief the alcoholic needs it. If it were not an addiction, the family member could easily gain insight into the self-destructive behavior and stop it.

Realizing that we, as family members, are free and not helpless victims can assure responsibility for ourselves. There are alternatives to pain. No matter how life is at present, there is strength to make choices for the better. As the process of recovery begins, better times are ahead. As the unhappy memories of the past, old arguments, obsessions with past relationships are diminished there is a greater achievement of one's own potentials for recovery.

ANECDOTE

"No One Can Move Mountains Alone"

"The first lesson. You cannot recover alone, no matter how independent you think you are. Recovery requires the insight and support of others. This point seems rather ironic since "reaching out to others", would seem a Herculean task to an adult child of an alcoholic. Once they do, somehow, decide to trust another person with their "story", there seems to be too much to talk about; feelings become overwhelming, often conflicting, or occurring simultaneously. Some adult children of alcoholics have numbed their feelings for so long, that they no longer know what they are feeling anymore.

It's important to talk about the past, but it is equally important for people to be careful not to get "stuck" there. Realize that your parents did the very best that they could. This doesn't mean they were perfect, or able to meet your needs, but that they tried. Just like you're trying to do now.

Another key ingredient to recovery, is to realize it's a process. And as part of that process, you must begin by recognizing the "little things" along the way. Recognize that you have needs and that they're important, just as important as anyone else's. Don't seek perfection; don't worry if you don't know why you are feeling a particular way. Just be glad you've progressed to the stage where you are able to actually identify your feelings. That's progress, and that's what recovering is all about. Learn how to express your opinions, whether they are hurt, anger, agreement or disagreement.

In order to recover, we must walk through our pain. Most adult children of alcoholics have the misconception that if they give up a little bit of control, chaos will break out. Fear of "losing it", going into a rage, saying things they "shouldn't", or crying uncontrollably is typical. The fact is, they've had to be in control for so long, that they're scared to let their guard down for even a minute.

The good news though is that no one has ever died of "overcrying;" it just doesn't happen. So let it out, find someone to talk to who can help you. Nothing is more important than your own well being!"

Laura B.

∎

Depression

Depression may manifest itself in ways other than extreme sadness. Fatigue is probably the most common symptom. There are many types of depressive disorders. Short periods of sadness, discouragement and even suicidal thinking are all part of normal living, particularly after losses or physical illness. These depressed moods usually last a few days and are not usually severe enough to interrupt the business of everyday life. In a reactional depression, the fatigue is associated with the work involved in completing the task. Once the work is over, normal energy levels resume. Almost everybody withdraws and tends to isolate. Some people will need more sleep, lose interest in themselves, and their appearance. The depressed person may be annoyed out of proportion. The smallest task seems beyond you. You feel a burden.

Suppressed emotions such as fear, anger, and hurt actually cause chemical changes to take place. It is the altered body chemistry that is responsible for the physical changes. It can happen the other way too. A physical change can cause depression. Poor nutrition, influenza, and hormonal changes such as at puberty, the menopause, and after childbirth, are all common causes of altered emotional states.

So often the sufferer will say "If I didn't feel so exhausted, I wouldn't be depressed." It is often the other way around. If there were no depression there would be no physical symptoms. Until you recognize that you are depressed, you cannot do anything about it.

Positive Acts to Raise Self-Esteem

1. Behave towards yourself as you would to a close friend.

2. Beware of self-pity. Don't wallow in it. Use a "stop thought" technique to change the way you are thinking. Some people talk it out on the telephone. Others may snap their fingers (the action or noise is the cue) to remove the confusing feelings.

3. Make time for yourself. Follow through with your plans.

4. Think about what you really want. Try to set realistic goals and time-frames.

5. Little treats may help. Try and be satisfied by the little things that you do well. Collect those memories.

6. Be good to yourself. Do something that will increase your self-image.

Sad Circumstances

It would be unnatural not to be depressed after the death of a relationship with a loved one, the loss of a job, or any other sad event. The sad person may be tearful and withdrawn. This phase should be regarded as the resting time when the sufferer is adjusting to the loss. Well-meaning friends often urge the sufferer not to cry. This is a mistake. Permission to grieve must be given. The pain or embarrassment of the onlookers should not be considered. Grief must not be repressed. It may emerge later as physical or depressive illness.

Some people recover from chronic depression when a skilled therapist uncovers childhood trauma such as rejection, sexual abuse, or lack of love. For many it is only necessary to accept that their depression comes from "listening to old tapes."

Since you were a child, your feelings about yourself have been formed from the opinions of those around you. These messages from the past should be left behind. They can be completely wrong or may have been misinterpreted by you. As an adult you can let go of the past, "old tapes", and other people's opinions of you and start being kind to yourself.

Obsessive self-interest will soon make you a tiresome person, but compassionate self-awareness is essential if the quality of life is to be improved. Low self-esteem is a major factor in depressive illness.

Physical work can cure depression. Although you may feel tired, the worst thing you can do is to stay in bed. Force yourself to get up early and eat. This helps to establish normal body rhythms and stops your turning day into night. Force yourself to walk no matter how tired your legs are. Get out of bed, put your feet on the floor, enter life. Living is an adventure, and each day will turn out different. It is your responsibility to join the life force. Exercise improves the circulation and stimulates anti-anxiety and anti-depressive influences.

Woodpecker Farms Lark

When you have made up you're mind *to close a relationship, you need to say goodbye.* For example, my black Labrador retriever had extensive health problems and I was going to have her put to sleep. She was a contributing family member, was excellent with children and always gentle. Lark was a tribute to this life. She was a constant companion for my daughter.

Labs like to swim and she had not been to the beach for years. When we arrived, I had to carry her across the sand wrapped in a blanket. She could hardly walk. I placed her in the water and tossed out a tennis ball. She loved it. Lark swam and retrieved the ball, alert and youthful, just like old times. We were both happy. She tired quickly. I had to carry her back to the car. A park ranger helped. Lark loved the ride home; she always liked to travel. We returned to the euthanasia room at the veterinary clinic.

We looked at each other and she knew. It was sad. I thanked her for being part of my life. We had said goodbye.

Explosive Rage

Poor impulse control and explosive rage are important causes of senseless assaults, killings without motives, self-injury, battery against wife or child, dangerously aggressive driving, divorce, and educational as well as social difficulties. Perhaps the greatest obstacle of the treatment process is in the acceptance and constructive resolution of anger.

Alcohol, a sedative drug, is one of a group of drugs that is often associated with violence. Amphetamines and cocaine also can produce hostilities with feelings of fear and paranoia. Should the stimulant user drink alcohol, the sedative effect can accentuate these emotional disturbances. The person using sedatives and stimulants in combination, may go explode with rage. Instead of feeling the effects of a single drug, the sedative may disinhibit the bottled up fears and release very unpredictable behavior. Alcohol and barbiturates must be avoided as they tend to increase aggressions. Many people can be taught to take evasive action by simply walking away from provocative situations.

--------------- QUOTATION ---------------
"As I lay awake at night in one of the rooms of my mother's house, I wonder if my father is going to make it home. Because once he does, I feel relief that society is safe for just one more night. But what if a drunk driver hits one of my family? I hate to say it, but if it were my father, instant justice."

ACOA

Mothers are often afraid they will hurt their children during these attacks. Losing your temper out of all proportion to the situation is distressing and very common. Children are most commonly abused by their own parents or others. The parents have often been abused themselves as children. The myth that a mother should be infinitely patient with a child may be deeply frustrating. When she finds herself incapable of being patient all day, hostilities may pile up. The alcoholic's liver usually lasts longer than the spouse, who tends to fall apart relatively early in the drinker's decline. Single parenting is common.

Disturbing behaviors by children may contribute to the abuse they receive. It is likely that irritable babies may be especially vulnerable to abuse. Children who are frustrating or stressful to their parents are the likely ones to be the victims of violence. The parents may also desire comfort and love themselves from children who are too young and immature to meet this expectancy.

The abusing parents have undergone too many changes in their lives at too rapid a pace. It appears that a rapid variety of stresses in a person's life is more difficult to adjust to than a single situational crisis such as divorce, loss of a job or sickness. The rapidity of stress situations appears to be the key to breakdowns in the abusing parents. They have no time to adjust from one shock before being confronted with a new crisis. The situation becomes overwhelming.

Excessive changes in stressful situations are not the only causes of child abuse. The abusing parents have difficulty getting their spouses to discipline the children and think of themselves as carrying the bigger burden in the family. Issues of discipline and decision making are often a source of frustration and anger. Many of the abusing parents can not get close to each other. They are distrusting and not likely to discuss problems.

Putting full blame on one parent serves little purpose. Both parents are involved even if only one does the abusing. In stressful situations that are precipitated by a child's behavior, it is the innocent child who becomes the primary focus of the abusing parent.

The symptoms of explosive rage are almost always the same. There are frequent episodes of intense rage, triggered by trivial irritations and accompanied by both verbal and physical violence, marked by explosive speech and profanity. The physical violence is apt to have a primitive quality.

Uncontrollable tempers sometimes run in families and as many as one-half of their children may show raging tempers. Children reared in an atmosphere of uncontrolled rage, quarrels between parents, and emotional deprivation are apt to become violent, but not all of them do so.

Children of alcoholics experience many self-esteem defeating incidents in their lives. The anger, abandonment, loss of control all lead to perpetuating low self-esteem. A life filled with inconsistencies is sure to be confusing. It would be a realistic effort not to further any lessened opinion of one's self. Many adult children of alcoholics should not bring up painful issues in the first year of recovery. It is more important to let the person stabilize.

Perpetuating Low Self-Esteem

1. "Everyone must love me." Not doing your own thinking and decision making. Requiring permission and approval of others. Believing you must prove yourself through superior performance.
2. "I must always be a nice person." Neglecting and ignoring your own needs in order to satisfy others. Being a "professional people pleaser". Doing things for others and not yourself.
3. "It's not my fault." Not accepting full responsibility for your own growth and well-being. Not developing your own talents and capabilities.
4. "I must be perfect." Setting your expectations too high, and therefore constantly being disappointed and finding fault with yourself would be a mistake.
5. "I'll never do anything right." Indulging in destructive self-criticism for your mistakes and failures.
6. "I must be perfectly secure." Not speaking up for your own convictions, letting others ignore and belittle you. Not realizing that no one can insult you unless you accept that person's authority over you.
7. "I have to be more impressive." Not letting others do things for you, or not believing that they might even want to.

——————————— QUOTATION ———————————

Codependency is defined as an "unconscious addiction to another persons's dysfunctional behavior."

Eleanor Williams

Codependence

Codependency is an unhealthy dependent pattern producing attitudes that make life painful. It is a dependency on people and things outside of oneself to the point of neglecting personal emotional needs and having little self-identity.

Family members may think that they have driven the alcoholic to drink and believe that they can control the alcoholics behavior. Most of the adult children of alcoholics feel they are somehow responsible for family problems. There is a tendency to put other people's needs before your own. It is a heavy burden. Intimacy is difficult.

For example, Jennie thought she could actually make a difference by cooking her husband better meals and by taking the kids out for drives on the weekends. Her next step was to hide her husband's liquor, which made him furious. Soon they were fighting almost daily. Jennie was wasting a lot of time and energy trying to change the past, while he kept getting worse.

Jim had an affair. Jennie found out and left. She took their five year old daughter. What all people need to learn is that the race is fixed. When there is no program of recovery, either through the support of a group or the self-imposed abstinence of an individual, the abused substance will always win, no matter what the competition.

Goddess with Flaws

Were you so powerless, Mother mine,
When YOU were a child?
That in my young mind burgeoning with
Tender sprouts of quick enquiry,
No curious germinating thought can be allowed
To grow. Entwine. Uproot
Or threaten the unstable pedestal
On which you stand.

But I am not an infant now.
And am I
(Like some well-trained canine
Taught to sit and beg, to whimper on command)
Am I,
According to the strange vicissitudes
Of every mood,
To give obedience without question to your wish,
So YOU can be assured of your control?
. . . I cannot let you bleed!

And so I laugh and clap my little hands
In pale felicity
To show my joy and cheer.
And you are reassured that all is well.
But I have died
Inside.

by Dorothy Gilham.

Despite their shared background of frequent conflicts and tensions, adult children of alcoholics usually look healthy and often perform well. But the survival techniques developed as children persist. They frequently have low self-esteem, guilt and depression. The children are different from the rest. They are different in that there are skills they don't have. They know how to be compliant, but not how to cooperate. They know how to handle a crisis or to do something at the last minute, but not how to do anything systematically. They are worried and concerned most of the time. They don't know how to relate to their peers, even though their peers like them. They don't know how to be friendly. Many of the adult children have a past or current drinking problem. There is no way that an adult child of an alcoholic ever takes a drink without being conscious of it; it means something.

In recent years more and more such adult children have banded together to confront the effects of parental alcoholism. In meetings modeled after Alcoholics Anonymous sessions, the adults focus on a different topic each meeting. For most, the pain of their chaotic upbringing has been buried under years of shame. Attendance at these self-help meetings nationwide is exploding.

During the last decade there has been an explosion of different treatment philosophy for the children of alcoholics. The therapeutic or group names change. For example, there is the organization called Adult Children of Alcoholics (ACA), Alanon, topics such as The Sense of Self in an Addicted Family, Treatment Methods for Shame Based Syndrome, or Stage 1 and 2 Recovery and many more. *All of these groups and philosophies are designed to help the victim of codependency discover the origins of their problems.*

_____ QUOTATION _____

"At this stage, the most important thing in my life is this program of recovery. Recovery is learning new tools, learning how to live. I let nothing interfere with it. When people come around who are real unhealthy and I think my program of recovery is threatened, I tell them good-bye. Right now, I'm just committed to getting better, to healing. And it's happening."

Lilly

The Beginning of Healing

Children raised by an alcoholic parent who is actively drinking or using drugs will have lots of memories. Adult children don't live, they relive. Most memories are repressed and there is a misconception of the rules they learned. Most children of all ages remain loyal to the dysfunctional parent. Therefore, part of recovery is visiting the past. It's not necessary to make a physical journey. Never take up permanent residence there. Looking at family pain may help someone discharge repressed emotions or resentments. Learning to recognize abnormal patterns begins to open the way to forgiveness and is a part of healing. *If the adult child is still preoccupied and obsessed with the past, the opportunities of the present are missed.* Identifying and working through past pain is essential. It is not a goal in itself. Face it, challenge it, learn from it, and move on.

A meaningful friendship is a long-term dialogue. If there is conflict or if we make a mistake or fail to do what our friend wants of us, we don't end the friendship. We simply have the next exchange to resolve the differences. Our dialogue continues over time. Time and amends build a bond. With it develops a deepening sense of reliability and trusting one another. As Robert Louis Stevenson said, "sit loosely in the saddle of life."

There are two reasonable choices. First, go back and share the pain and the feelings that have long festered. Then you can choose to say good-bye to either the issues or the people involved. Remember, this doesn't have to be done in person. Second, you can choose to forgive, to ask for forgiveness, and then work on reestablishing relationships. There are choices in recovery. Staying stuck, feeling powerless, and postponing action are part of the illness.

Forgiving brings great healing. You can begin by forgiving yourself for being such a "burden". Anger, hate, resentment, all dissolve when there is real forgiveness. The statement, "I will never forgive him/her" really means that the immaturity in your make-up is sulking. Forgiveness is another word for letting go.

_____ NOTES _____

"Dear Dad, I want you to know we've been through some hard times but, you've always been here for me. Thank you for everything. You taught me a bunch. I love you. Jaime"

"Hello, I'm so happy that you are doing better now and what's been between us is now fading away, so once again I appreciate you as my father and my friend. Love, Patrick"

Forgiveness

Forgiveness is an emotional experience. It brings back the past and projects into the future. It remembers and it forgets.

We remember good qualities such as love, kindness, patience, thoughtfulness and perhaps a host of other emotional responses of the past that are treasured and kept intact in memory.

We forget troublesome recollections, petulant reactions, angry confrontations, rejections of other viewpoints and dozens of characteristics that are best laid to rest as the will to forgive develops.

Alcohol and drugs are powerful forces for destruction of self and family. Often there are monstrous difficulties to be resolved. The downward spiral in family relationships may cease only after recovery is well founded. Recovery opens the door to forgiveness, however any resemblance of mercy may be beyond reach. Addictive disease produces trash. Garbage is disease producing and should be handled with utmost care to prevent self-infestation, or discarded. Should a rose bloom from this discarded human waste, now that's a sight to behold. Forgiveness is taking the risk to approach the rose and smell its fragrance.

―――――――――――― QUOTATION ――――――――――――

"Children begin by loving their parents; as they grow older they judge them; sometimes they forgive them."

Oscar Wilde

The Normal Psychological Development of the American Teenager

A physician of the Department of Psychiatry of the University of California School of Medicine at Los Angeles observes the psychological development

that occurs at this time of life can be organized into developmental tasks, which emphasize the purposefulness of adolescence. Dr. Lewis Judd states that to understand teenagers there should be comprehension of the process and purpose of adolescence itself. Nine tasks confront youth from ages 11 to 21.

1. The establishment of independence from parents and other adults. During normal adolescence there is resistance to the influence and opinions of parents. The adolescent becomes more skeptical, more argumentative, opinionated, and negativistic. The child is a poor listener.

2. The arrival at a stable self-concept or self-definition. The establishment of a stable identity is probably one of the more basic tasks of growing up. The adolescent comes to recognize capabilities and weaknesses, and is apt to experiment with a multitude of roles and choices.

3. The development of self-motivation and self-determination. It is necessary for the adolescent to be able to rely on him or herself as a primary source for personal initiative and direction. Young people show increasing resistance and reluctance to act when adults try to oversee or direct their behavior.

4. The establishment of an appropriate set of values. By establishing an appropriate set of values the adolescent acquires the concepts and rules of conduct that are necessary for living in a society as an adult.

5. The development of understanding and sympathy for others and of reciprocity in interpersonal relationships. The ability to feel tenderness, respect, and concern for others is a major step in emotional development. It involves being able to achieve one's own goals without trampling on the rights of others.

6. The establishment of an appropriate sexual identity and the development of wholesome relationships with members of the opposite sex. The unreadiness of adolescents is often expressed through their unhappiness with their own physical characteristics. There is always something they obsessively wish could be changed, such as their complexion, height, weight, body proportions, facial features, or almost anything.

7. The development of new intellectual capacities and skills. Abstract thinking, perspectives of past and future, and intellectual functioning are apt to be very close to adult levels by the age of 16 years.

8. The development of the ability to function satisfactorily with age mates and to behave properly with others in the peer group. Most adolescents conform. Nonconformists are rejected and ridiculed. The adolescent group usually has its own music, style of dress, language, and values. The ability to function within this adolescent society is necessary to gain appropriate social rewards.

9. The acquisition of training, or participation in a training program, that will develop skills for achieving economic independence. The development of self-reliance is an essential step on the part of the adolescent for supporting a family. The completion of this task signals the end of adolescence.

Adolescence—When Isn't it "Just a Phase"

Despite much popular opinion most adolescents do not need treatment by a specialist and most will function competently. However there are five clues as to whether or not an adolescent needs professional assistance for better adjustments.

These clues are as follows:

1. Family Relationships. It is important to sort out family disturbances as well as individual adolescent problems. Do any arguments linger in resentment and anger or do they subside as in normal families? Are there particular family stresses?

2. Relationships with Friends. Does the adolescent have friends or is there excessive shyness and loneliness? By middle adolescence sexual interests should be significant and by late adolescence dating should have started. The average adolescent can describe a best friend ably and in depth. The more disturbed youngster's description is apt to have one characteristic only — a flat, monotonous quality.

3. School Performance. Examination of school grades in respect to intellect and family expectations may uncover inhibitions, anxieties, frustrations, poor control of impulses, depressions or various conflicts that consume energies. Has there been truancy or general withdrawal? Is there an interest in extracurricular activities?

4. Extracurricular Activities. The average adolescent does not spend time in prolonged, idle boredom, but can and does participate in sports, hobbies or other activities in and out of school with friends and groups.

5. Indicators of Abnormality. Disturbed adolescents are apt to be involved in anti-social or self-destructive behaviors. Has the child been in trouble with the law, property destruction, assaults, drug abuse, promiscuity, running away or other similar behaviors?

Crucial points of behavior need to be reviewed and understood if they are of sufficient intensity to merit professional help. Problems must be confronted with sympathy and understanding in a non-punitive way, but with a clear direct manner.

Adolescence is a time of life marked by emotional turmoil and turbulence which create problems for the adolescent, the family and society in general. These are normal developmental tasks. Large numbers of adults leave adolescence without having achieved emotional or economic independence. Thus, in our society there are many adults who are still struggling with "adolescent" problems. The teenager is undergoing substantial change without the aggravations of an alcoholic parent. Children of alcoholics will be confronted with family problems in addition to the turmoil of growing up. It's hard. Perhaps parents can better remember their own adolescence through a review of normal developmental tasks. Maybe your child is not weird at all; they may be like their parents used to be. *Adults must judge adolescence by its own processes and purpose, not by adult standards.*

The Nine Convicts

Alcoholics take hostages. They may marry and raise a family but they're all emotional hostages. Escape is possible. Consider the following convicts confronted with a life or death sentence.

During the Irish revolution of 1848, nine young men were captured, tried and convicted of treason against the Queen. The sentence was death. The presiding judge read out the names of the condemned men: Charles Duffy, Thomas Meager, Patrick Donahue, Terence McManus, Richard O'-Gorman, Morris Lyene, Michael Ireland, Thomas McGee, John Mitchell. Have you anything to say before the court passes sentence?

Thomas Meagher had been chosen to speak for them all. "My Lord, this is our first offense, but not our last, if you will be easy with us this once, we promise on our word as gentlemen to try to do better next time, and the next time we sure won't be fools enough to get caught." The indignant judge sentenced them to be hanged by the neck, but passionate protests from all over the world caused Queen Victoria to commute the sentence. The men were transported for life to the penal colony that was then savage Australia.

In 1871, a Sir Charles Duffy was elected prime minister of the Australian state of Victoria. To her amazement, Queen Victoria learned from her prime minister Disraeli that this was the same Charles Duffy who had been transported for treason 23 years before. She demanded the records of the other eight convicts and this is what she learned.

Thomas Meagher was Governor of Montana, Patrick Donahue and Terence McManus were Brigadier Generals in the U.S. Army. Richard O'-Gorman was Governor General of New Foundland. Morris Lyene was Attorney General of Australia to which office Michael Ireland succeeded. Thomas McGee was president of the Dominion of Canada and John Mitchell was a prominent New York politician whose son later became Mayor of New York City.[1]

This amazing true story of nine men who were at first sentenced to death, but were later banished from their native land to a penal colony for their political views, and years later became outstanding citizens in America,

Australia, and Canada, is now a part of the United States Congressional Record in Washington, D.C.

Summary

Alcoholism can have serious effects on all members of a family. Children, in particular, may represent hidden tragedies. They are not to blame for the chemical dependency of a parent and that should be a starting point for their own comprehension of the situation. Recovery from childhood and adolescent depressions and despairs are possible and should be worked on. Concentration on school activities can be helpful and learnings achieved may be of lifetime value. Sports and other school activities may alleviate loneliness and help in daily adjustments. Children need not be helpless victims in an alcoholic family. Responsibilities for their own development can and should be assumed. Sadness, depression and tearfulness are normal and forgivable expressions under the circumstances. These sad reactions are commonplace for children in alcoholic families, but they can be countered by the victims themselves if better understandings can be reached. Suggestions are offered in this chapter.

Self-Test

1. The number of school children with a parent who is alcoholic or on drugs has been calculated as one in: (A) ten; (B) eight; (C) six; (D) three; (E) two.

2. In the alcoholic family the child is apt to: (A) feel unloved; (B) be spoiled; (C) have superior grades; (D) be like children in non-alcoholic families; (E) none of the foregoing.

3. Identify the step or steps in the process of recovery in children of alcoholics: (A) acknowledge the little things; (B) recognize that fears are greater than reality; (C) don't bottle feelings up; (D) set clear limits, know your boundaries; (E) all of the foregoing.

4. The children in an alcoholic family: (A) are apt to be overlooked and may represent a hidden tragedy; (B) are best not involved in treatment programs; (C) are encouraged most if the alcoholic parent returns home immediately after treatment; (D) feel more secure if the mother, rather than the father, is the alcoholic; (E) all of the foregoing.

5. Wives of alcoholics: (A) are often evasive and uncooperative; (B) may withhold information; (C) sometimes resent examination of their own relationship to the situation; (D) may come to resemble an alcoholic; (E) all of the foregoing.

6. Adolescent children of an alcoholic family may: (A) be disturbed by family arguments; (B) be shy and lonely; (C) exhibit anti-social and self-destructive behaviors; (D) leave home; (E) all of the foregoing.

7. Alcoholism is sometimes related to: (A) aggression against a spouse or children; (B) dangerously aggressive driving; (C) divorce; (D) the death of a relationship; (E) all of the foregoing.

8. The beginning of healing and recovery does involve: (A) visiting the past; (B) living in the past as the opportunities of the present are missed; (C) the acceptance and constructive resolution of anger; (D) forgiveness is another word for letting go; (E) all of the forgoing.

Answers: 1(D); 2(A); 3(E); 4(A); 5(E); 6(E); 7(E); 8(E)

Notes

1. Michael J. McCabe, Sr., Los Angeles County Historian, A.O.H.

Bibliography

1. Woter, Dwight Lee. *A Life Worth Waiting For*, 241 pp. Compcare Publishers, MN. 1989.
2. Wegscheider-Cruz, Sharon. *The Miracle of Recovery*. 212 pp. Health Communications, Inc., Deerfield Beech, FL. 1989.
3. Brown, Stephanie. *Treating Adult Children of Alcoholics*. 333pp. John Wiley and Sons, Inc., New York, New York, 1988.
4. Seixas, Judith S. and Youcha, Geraldine. *Children of Alcoholism*. 208 pp. Harper and Row, New York, New York 1985.
5. Wegscheider-Cruz, Sharon. *Choicemaking*. 217 pp. Health Communications, Inc., Deerfield Beech, FL. 1985.
6. Woititz, Janet G. *Adult Children of Alcoholics*. 106 pp. Health Communications, Inc., Deerfield Beech, FL. 1983
7. Black, Claudia. *Children of Alcoholics*. 203 pp. Vallantine Books, New York, New York. 1981.

Cocaine and Other Street Stimulants

Introduction

A broad-based cocaine abuse epidemic has occurred in the United States throughout the 1980's, the peak of which is not yet in sight. Cocaine, once considered an upper-and-middle-class drug, has now crossed social class lines and is becoming more popular within the lower class. The popularity of crack provides an excellent example. The age of cocaine onset has dropped, so that adolescent cocaine abuse problems are part of the pattern.

There is also an increasing prevalence of rapid delivery forms of cocaine, including free-basing and injection, as well as using the drug along with other types. Most cocaine users also abuse other drugs, the most common being alcohol.

Cocaine dependence has the characteristics of a similar addictive disease, alcoholism. However, cocaine dependence has different toxic, cultural, and legal consequences than alcoholism. Cocaine addiction has the characteristics of a chronic, relapsing and fatal disease.

The Users of Stimulants

David Smith M. D., founder and Director of the Haight-Ashbury Free Medical Clinic in San Francisco, California estimates than 25 million people have used cocaine and that 5 million are dysfunctional.

It is estimated that of every 100 people who use cocaine once, approximately 10 to 20 percent will develop cocaine addiction. In addition, another 30 to 40 percent will have some dysfunction at least once in their lives. The adverse effects can destroy careers as people lose interest in work and spend all their money on the drug. Use of the drug can ruin family life as users alienate loved ones and undergo drastic personality changes withdrawing into a world in which their only contacts are other coke users and their only interest is getting more. *Cocaine is cold. It isolates. People talk past each other.*

Cocaine

Cocaine is an anesthetic and a stimulant when used clinically. When used recreationally, it can be a poison. The dosage is uncontrolled and all of the "cutting" agents are unknown to the consumer. Yet, each day an estimated 5,000 people try it for the first time according to the National Institute of Drug Abuse (NIDA). Of those, an estimated 20 percent may become addicted. Roughly 365,000 new cocaine addicts step over the line each year. These totally unpredictable addictions lead them down an unexplored trail unexperienced by most people. It is punctuated by the loss of family, friends, self-respect, employment, values and the triad of physical, emotional, and spiritual health.

─────────────── QUOTATION ───────────────

" . . . *We are having epidemic levels of the destructive use of cocaine. . .* "

Nicholas J. Kozel and Edgar Adams
National Institute of Drug Abuse, 1985.

A clinical professor of psychiatry at UCLA reports that the Inca Indians used cocaine 3,000 years ago in the high mountains of Peru and Bolivia. At first, the coca leaves from which the cocaine is obtained were a drug of the ruling classes. Later, the Spanish conquistadors discovered that the chewing of coca leaves enabled the poverty-stricken Indians living in the highlands to survive work in the mines despite a scarcity of food and the cold, thin atmosphere.

About 100 years ago, when cocaine was extracted from coca leaves, it was first thought that the drug would be able to cure addiction to morphine and alcohol. This belief soon subsided, but by the beginning of the 20th century many patent medicines and soft drinks contained a little cocaine. The Pure Food and Drug Law controlled this practice.

At present, the Coca-Cola Company takes the cocaine out of the imported leaves and turns it over to the government for medical use. Medically, it is the only naturally occurring topical anesthetic used as a nasal or throat spray to deaden nerves when intubating patients. It is also used in some eye surgery. It abolishes the sensation of taste and smell.

Cocaine produces a condition of excessive stimulation. Feelings of great power dominate, although restlessness and unpleasant tensions associated with paranoid thinking may follow. The effects of cocaine are of short duration, and depression may follow its discontinuation. This depression may be due to the depletion of certain chemical reserves in the body. Heavy use of cocaine leads to a loss of weight, sleeplessness, and anxiety reactions. Paranoid thinking, hallucinations and delusions occur. Sometimes the addict may believe that bugs are crawling under the skin. Violent behavior may occur, but because of the short duration of effects sustained aggressions seldom occur.

In the mid-seventies, a couple of street chemists discovered a way to lower the melting point of cocaine through a simple chemical process so it could efficiently be heated, vaporized and smoked. This is known as "freebasing", which is usually the smoking of pure cocaine rather than the hydrochloride salt or any of the substances used to "step" or "cut" the original amount. Ether or baking soda is used to make freebase.

Pharm Chem Labs test samples from the "streets" and reveal about 30 percent cocaine purity. The rest can be anything. The freebasing of cocaine removes most "cuts". Certain ingredients are more difficult to eliminate. Even the "chlorox" test will reveal the impurity by a change in color or different patterns produced by the powder. Pure cocaine would float on top of this bleaching agent. A line of cocaine (50% purity) is about 1 1/2 inches long, and 1/8 inches wide and contains between 5–15 mg. of the drug. It's possible that 20 mg. can kill you.

Pure wholesale pharmaceutical cocaine (Malenckrodt "flake") retails for an average of $68.52 per ounce. Street cocaine, on the other hand, is sold for between $80 to $100 per gram. There are 28 grams per ounce. Expensive coke habits can cost up to $300 to $500 dollars a day. One unfortunate result of the expensive price is that the user may become a dealer to finance the cocaine habit, risking potential arrest, imprisonment and loss of employment as well as destruction of whatever reputation the person may have established. Cocaine abusers typically are in financial difficulties, and have problems with family members and their work, where capacities for good performance are apt to decline. If the cocaine is high quality, the cost may go up.

Cocaine or Crack?

Crack is a form of preprocessed cocaine. Reports on novel ways to get high travel fast, as is apparent from the popularity of crack. This cheap and wildly addictive way to smoke cocaine is a drug nightmare. For example, you can go out and buy some hamburger, bring it home and cook it yourself. Or, you can go to McDonalds and buy one of theirs. The Golden Arches Laboratory and Grill has done the cooking and preparation. Street chemistry has come up with a purified, highly potent, cocaine distillate known as "crack". Therefore, you can prepare your own freebase, or buy someone else's. The business operates like a fast food franchise. "Crack" cocaine can be sold in any quantity.

George R. Gay, M.D. from the Emergency Medicine and Rock Medicine Section of the Haight-Ashbury Free Medical Clinic worked out this clever comparison between cocaine and crack. In practical terms, one "line" of street coke weighs between 5 mg. and 10 mg. The cocaine contained depends on percentage of purity. If the material at hand were 50 percent purity, then "one gram," injected or snorted over whatever time, would equal 500 mg. of cocaine. "Freebasing" or smoking of the base in a small pipe, usually involves a single "hit," or dosage, of less than a "fifteenth" (1/15 of a gram, or about 67 mg; a "tenth" would be 100 mg). Pure cocaine (base or freebase) is a colorless, odorless, transparent crystalline substance that is almost totally insoluble in water but freely soluble in dimethyl ether. Further, the melting point of freebase is much lower than that of its salt (98 C). In the form of its hydrochloride salt, cocaine is a white crystalline powder with a melting point of 195 C.

The crack itself has been freebased and a flammable material (dimethyl ether) has been mixed together with the cocaine. It is also made by mixing cocaine hydrochloride with a solution of baking soda or ammonia in water. The mixture is heated and the water evaporates, leaving a hard crystalline paste that can be cut into premeasured chips or "rocks." The user can make a $5–20 purchase, heat up the hard crystalline paste until a cocaine vapor appears and smoke it. The process of making crack doesn't eliminate the impurities or the substances used to cut the original cocaine, so contamination is a risk. The means of packaging in precisely measured crystals at affordable units makes it easier to transport and sell. Crack has spread faster than other drugs on the street. The name "crack" appears to come from the cracking sound made by the solution while it is being processed or smoked.

The "crack" market has introduced the Black community to the drug, where a majority of "crack" addiction and illegal drug sales take place. The advantage of crack over free-base is that it is processed into smokeable form prior to sale and that amounts of the drug can be fairly exact. This means that the cocaine smoker no longer has to operate a chemical lab in order to convert street cocaine into free-base. It also means that dealers can sell small quantities of the drug at a low price. It's all a matter of economics. The person purchasing small amounts of crack can usually find another $20. At the end of a day's run, maybe $100 or more has been spent. Small amounts of money goes down the same sewer as big money.

Some pregnant women use "crack" to induce an abortion. Use of the drug early in pregnancy, the first trimester, is the worst time to attempt spontaneous abortion. Abortion is not usually associated with smoking "crack" early in pregnancy, but it does induce labor later in pregnancy. "Crack" and numerous other drugs may deform the baby, especially in the early developmental period. The pregnant woman may abandon the use of "crack" as a way to induce labor early in her pregnancy, and give birth to a deformed baby affected with long term neurological damage. "Crack"-cocaine babies experience more fetal wastage, abruptio placenta (a premature detachment of the placenta prior to delivery of the infant), anorectic effects, deficient nutrition, and intra-uterine strokes.

So addictive is crack cocaine, that the dealer will be asked to take anything in exchange for the drug. Cash is standard, sexual favors are offered, and other services or items of value. Addicts will do anything for a piece of the rock and may take more drastic measures, including violence, to get their crack. Someone who has "tweaked out" has obviously been a chronic user of cocaine. Normal thinking processes have been disturbed. This type of addict is dangerous and may go to any lengths to obtain the drug.

Some drugs, including cocaine, have a greater potential for compulsive use and are more likely to trigger addiction. The drugs include the narcotic-analgesics, the short-acting barbiturates (such as amobarbital, pentobarbital, and secobarbital), cocaine, crack and fentanyl. They have a quick, powerful onset of action which probably strongly stimulates repetitive use. For example, cash is more likely than work to trigger a binge in someone with a spending addiction.

The potential for producing designer-cocaine may mean that this drug problem won't be solved just by tightening our borders. A crackdown on imported cocaine could make the synthetic version cost-effective.

MDMA

There are also synthetic cocaine-like stimulants, MDMA, or "ecstasy." This is a designer drug of a very different sort, a derivative of an amphetamine and a hallucinogen. The designer drug phenomenon, still in its early stages, has a tremendous potential for causing widespread destruction across the nation. The drug potencies are fantastic. Dosage variations occur by adding or deleting a molecule. MDMA is also known as "adam," MDME is an analog drug known as "eve". Many labs are set up in rural areas of Texas and other states, mostly exporting the drug to California. Their toxic effects are bizarre and unpredictable.

Bill had taken MDMA three weeks ago, his thoughts drifting from reality to fantasy. He was concerned when the drug's effect would end. The Haight-Ashbury detox center in San Francisco advised him to get lots of exercise and drink fruit juices. It was impossible to measure the strength of the street batch of MDMA and since no one could get "inside his head," he would have to control the trip himself. Bill told me that he thought "ecstacy" would "make sex better and he would have insight while doing it." His thinking would get better with time, so long as he didn't have a *dual diagnosis*. The patient suffering from chemical dependency and a co-existing psychiatric problem such as schizophrenia, manic depressive illness, or depression is considered to have more than one problem. *Drugs may activate psychiatric disease, an additional illness that could have remained dormant.* Crack can do it as well.

Speed of Action

The speed of action depends on the way a drug is taken. The slowest method is drinking, or oral ingestion. It takes about 20 minutes for the drug to reach the central nervous system. Blood levels of cocaine were found to be highest in persons who had swallowed the drug. Autopsies disclose congestion and swelling of abdominal tissues and small hemorrhages. If chewed and absorbed through the gum or snorted, the route is shorter, the onset of action about three to five minutes. If injected the action starts even faster. It takes fifteen to thirty seconds for cocaine to reach the brain. The fastest route, about eight seconds, is smoking, either freebase or crack.

Cocaine works directly on the brain and produces an addiction that is more powerful than that from heroin. Effects on the brain have been well verified. In one survey, it was found that 12 percent of the coke users had suffered from convulsions at least once. Among heavy users, 22 percent reported loss of consciousness. Over 60% of both male and female cocaine users have suffered from sexual dysfunction at one time of another. Chronic use leads to ejaculatory and orgasmic failure, a reversible condition.

—————————— QUOTATION ——————————
"There is absolutely no doubt that cocaine is one of the most powerfully addictive drugs known. . . "
                                                Donald J. MacDonald, M.D., 1985.

Cocaine is a powerful constrictor of blood vessels, and it is this feature of the drug that causes ulcerations of tissues of the nose when high doses are used for "snorting". Additionally, this constriction raises blood pressure twenty to thirty points. Cocaine also stimulates and changes the heart muscle as it passes through the coronary arteries and heart chambers. Cardiac abnormalities may include: rapid heart beats, extra heart beats, ventricular tachycardia or even death. Other effects on the body will occur but the greatest effects will occur as the coke passes through the blood-brain barrier. This protects the central nervous system, the brain and spinal cord, from infusion with dangerous or unwanted substances. Psycho-active drugs, such as cocaine, will breach this defense.

Kindling Effect

As with amphetamines, a kindling effect occurs with cocaine following a period of abstinence when the individual repeatedly begins using small doses of cocaine. The user may experience the same intense physiological response as with the larger doses of past use, leading to neurological or psychiatric symptoms, including seizures or cardiac arrest. Treatment is often unnecessary because reactions are over before the patient arrives for treatment. Many of the cocaine overdose deaths have been relapse deaths, following a period of abstinence in an episodic cocaine abuse. There is death at both high and low-dose use. The addict will relapse faster and harder! This effect occurs with both street stimulants and alcohol. Stimulants produce a dramatic, attention getting effect, while alcohol travels at a more relaxed pace. Alcohol is more subtle and patient. It can be measured in months. Nevertheless, the Kindling Effect has been activated. The coronor's report shows time and again that a recovering addict, about two to three months clean, who returns to controlled use ends up dead from low doses. There is some kind of post-synaptic mind sensitivity, somewhat like an allergic response. *You can't cheat nature without paying the price.*

Four Stanford University medical scientists have published a report on the effects of cocaine on the heart. Dr. Henry Tazellar and his associates examined the heart tissue of 30 persons who had died because of the use of cocaine. The cause of death was confirmed with autopsies performed by the Coroner of San Francisco. In 28 of these addicts, the heart had red streaks in the muscle fibers that marked a condition of permanent contraction that made the cells useless. These dead cells are not only useless in themselves, but block the normal functioning of other muscle fibers and nerve-conduction tissues. The drug can cause serious cardiac damage that may end in death.

Signs and symptoms of the effect of cocaine may appear as a chest pain, a disturbed rhythm of the heart, a typical heart attack and even sudden death. An insufficient flow of blood to heart tissues, the spasm of vessels that supply the heart with blood and oxygen, the replacement of normal heart muscle by fibrous infiltration may precede the final effects of cocaine. Even in small amounts, cocaine may injure the heart and be a cause of death.

Do the Damaging Effects of Cocaine Disappear Once its Use Has Been Discontinued?

Since the 1970s, the use of cocaine has increased at disturbing rates. Currently, one of every six high school seniors have used cocaine at least once and almost 7 percent of young adults have used the drug at some time in the previous month. The introduction of "crack" cocaine has contributed to the continuing epidemic of street stimulants.

Damaging effects from the use of cocaine during the 1970s are now appearing in epidemic proportions. The three most severe effects of cocaine on the brain in this delayed appearance appear to be: (1) loss of consciousness; (2) convulsions; and (3) death. Physicians are finding that in many persons the foregoing consequences do not occur until after 3 to 4 years of drug usage.

Neurochemistry and Addiction

The target of cocaine, the central nervous system, normally acts as a combination switchboard and computer-analyzing information system from the peripheral nervous system. It decides on a response, then reroutes the incoming information to the appropriate system, muscle or organ. The central nervous system uses a system of about one-hundred-billion nerve cells to perform these functions.

Because none of these nerve cells touch each other directly, a combination of electrical and chemical signals are needed to get the message across. The message, an impulse, travels electrically to a minute junction between nerve cells called a synapse. There it causes tiny bits of chemicals, called neurotransmitters to be released to carry the appropriate information across the synaptic cleft or "gap". These neurotransmitters slot into receptor sites on the adjacent cell, triggering an electrical relay of the signal to the next synapse where the process is repeated. The neurotransmitters, which have returned to the holding sack, are released again.

Distorted messages being sent to the body, heart, lungs, and especially the brain may cause malfunctioning. Fear is one of the messages particularly susceptible to manipulation when cocaine is involved. Other messages involve passion, conflict, and athletic performance. In each of these cases, the body calls for additional energy and action. Extra neurotransmitters are required to prepare the body to react quickly to the danger or pleasure at hand.

When the extra energy is no longer needed or the danger has passed, the neurotransmitters reabsorb or are neutralized. When cocaine is taken, it forces release of neurotransmitters. In addition, the cocaine blocks intake ports of the transmitting nerve cells so energy chemicals cannot be reabsorbed when they return across the synaptic gap. And so they stay free longer, exaggerating the extra energy signal. Cocaine rewards the user chemically. Remember, the extra energy is a loan and must be paid back. An addict on a "run" will crash and sleep for a prolonged time.

Neurotransmitters must be in balance for the body to function normally. If one becomes depleted, the others become unbalanced. For example, some of the neurotransmitters affected by cocaine are dopamine, acetylcholine, and serotonin. Unbalanced dopamine can cause a person to become overly suspicious, paranoid and delusional. Excessive levels of acetylcholine, cause muscle tremors, involuntary muscular reflexes and memory lapses. When finally depleted, mental confusion and even hallucinations may result.

Normally, serotonin helps us sleep and keeps us from being depressed but as cocaine is used over a longer period of time, serotonin becomes depleted, causing insomnia, agitation, and depression. The disruption of the chemical balance can cause the physical exhaustion and depression to persist for days, weeks and even months.

Nutritional Supplements

Other neurotransmitters such as epinephrine and norepinephrine tend to cause excitement and their release is stimulated by cocaine. The cocaine addict's brain is not foggy (as in the alcoholic) and it's important to get addicts involved in education, exercise, a balanced diet with certain nutritional supplements and a chemical-free group process.

The role of amino acids is also important in cocaine recovery. Research indicates that the amino acids L-tryptophan and tyrosine are deficient in cocaine users, and replacing these substances can actually reduce the desire for cocaine. Serotonin is manufactured from L-tryptophan. The Federal Drug Administration suspended the sale of L-tryptophan in January of 1990. Tyrosine is also helpful in restoring chemical balance. It occurs in a mixed amino acid supplement and contains 15 to 17 amino acids in one formula, 400 mg three times a day for one to four weeks is an adequate dose. Nutritional supplements can be found at health food stores. Additional B vitamins are helpful, especially B-1, B complex, and C as well. These vitamins, as well as other substances, are known to be involved in the healing process of the mind. There are many other nutritional supplements that may be prescribed by a physician that can help restore normal chemical balance.

Most of the effects of cocaine toxicity, dependence and withdrawal can be explained by the cocaine-induced release and inhibition of neurotransmitters to the brain as well as depletion of cocaine. The agitation, restlessness and anxiety are likely effects of norepinephrine hyperactivity, while paranoia, delusions and hallucinations are probable effects of dopamine hyperactivity. The cocaine addict's brain is out of order, and physical well-being may be irreversibly damaged. The use of nutrional supplements help the body and mind regain balance and can aid in normal thought processes. Nothing takes away cues and drug hunger but hard work. The later part of chapter seven should be taken seriously! Taking vitamins and anti-depressants can help, but they will not cure you. As you know, there is no cure, only a program of action to take you away from misery. If you don't enjoy getting better, the pain can be refunded immediately.

"How Long Does Cocaine Remain in the Body?"

Cocaine has one of the shortest detection periods: 12 to 72 hours following use."[1]

"Can Any Medication Other Than Cocaine Cause a Positive Cocaine Test Result?

Absolutely not. This includes local anesthetics, such as benzocaine, xylocaine and lidocaine, used by dentists."[1]

There are other problems that occur with long term use of cocaine. One is infection from contaminants from using the drug intravenously. Damaging microbial infections, such as endocarditis, and blood infections such as septic shock or hepatitis are common.

Further there is increasing evidence of AIDS caused by sharing dirty coke needles and injecting freebase is a major vehicle in which this disease is spread. Another danger is tissue that dies or becomes gangrenous because of severely restricted blood flow caused by cocaine's ability to constrict blood vessels. This occurs most often at the injection site or the nose. The nasal septum may become perforated because of dissolved cartilage.

Adulteration is a problem with any drug bought from a street dealer. Cocaine is subdivided from a kilogram or a pound into lesser weights, being "stepped-on" (diluted with adulterants) by each dealer in its economic chain. It is cut with various sugars (mannitol, lactose, glucose, inositol) for volume and weight and with salts of various commercial synthetic local anesthetics (lidocaine, procaine, tetracaine) for the taste. Lidocaine and tetracaine also give a "freeze" when topically tested on mucous membranes. Less common adulterants are caffeine, benzocaine, amphetamine, heroin, phencyclidine, and quinine.

Several methods of rapid street sample analysis are now employed by wary customers. These include personal biological sampling, use of a "hot box", determining melting point, and methanol and Clorox solubility.

The principle difference between cocaine and speed (methamphetamine) is that "crank" lasts a much longer time in the body and stimulates you for a much greater period of time. Speed does not provide the same degree of stimulation and euphoria as does cocaine. Both drugs are euphoric, but cocaine lasts about forty minutes duration while speed lasts four to six hours duration of action.

With cocaine in particular, the stimulation can be so intense that a downer, such as alcohol, some strong pot, a benzodiazepine (a tranquilizer such as Xanax or Valium), heroin, Seconal, is needed to take the edge off of the high. Instead of laying in bed sweating all night, the user wouldn't be as jittery or grinding away their teeth.

Denial can be unbelievable. Families still believe that periodontal grinding plates will help the grinding away of teeth caused by methamphetamine addiction, episodic use is less serious than chronic use and that alcoholism is more acceptable than use of street stimulants.

ANECDOTE

Brent was married and had four children. His full-time job paid about $20,000 gross. He decided to supplement his income by dealing cocaine. The cash generated by dealing supported his personal addiction. At least that's what he thought. He used up more than he sold. Brent soon felt trapped. Less than three years later, he found himself locked in a walk-in closet, basing cocaine. His children knocked on the door. "Daddy, why are you always locked in there?" Brent voluntarily entered treatment for a freebase addiction.

Money generated by selling drugs can also be a trap. Here's what this dealer-addict said, "Like taking crack, selling it can also be very addictive. When you start dealing and you make so much money, when you want to stop you can't. You start to say, I made $300 today, so I can make $500 the next day, and so on."

Before leaving treatment, Brent withdrew $5,000 cash from his savings prior to visiting hours. He had obtained a two hour pass. Even a fool knows you can't spend that amount of money in the vending machines. One of his friends was coming to see how he was doing. This friend left with a lot of cash. Brent didn't respond to treatment, but he was exposed. He was just going to sell, not smoke. Brent told me that he kept about 80 percent of the cash for business, gave his family 10 percent and used 10 percent for sex. Some of the girls he gave crank to just couldn't be satisfied. Compulsive income addiction shows how devious chemical addictions can be, so repeated exposures to treatment are sometimes required. Some people stop dealing through death.

∎

General Conclusions About Stimulants

Some general conclusions that can be made about stimulants are: 1) they are attractive to people who are psychologically depressed; 2) overdoses are rare (except for cocaine and crank); 3) an increase in blood pressure may rupture a weak part of the circulatory system, such as an aneurysm; 4) tolerance will develop, but not cross tolerance; 5) an anorectic or anti-appetite effect develops which lasts prior to tolerance, thus ultimately appetite returns. Examples of drugs which would conform to this profile would be cocaine, crack, amphetamines, methamphetamine (speed, crank), and an assortment of other drugs.

Methamphetamine

The person who uses high-dose methamphetamine is seeking the "rush". In other words, once the substance is taken there is a very rapid reaction. As explained before, the route of administration will influence the speed of the drug effect. The drug can be taken in a variety of ways. It can be added to your coffee, it can be snorted or injected. It's known as "crank" on the streets, but as with any illicit drug, names will vary. "Speed," "Crystal Meth," and "L.A. Glass" are but three.

Crank is becoming the hottest selling drug in blue collar areas. And according to officials at the Drug Enforcement Administration, it is quickly replacing cocaine or crack, especially in some parts of the country like the Pacific coast and the Southwest.

Federal drug officials estimate that underground chemists will produce as much as 25 tons of crank this year to supply the 1.5 to 2 million users in the United States. Mobile labs are being equipped. The smell produced through "cooking" the drug can be diverted. Large recreational vehicles are sometimes the site of the manufacturing plant, being driven over long stretches of freeway at 55 mph.

Methamphetamine interrupts sleep patterns and suppresses appetite. The individual may go on a "speed binge" lasting from three to four days during which the addict "shoots up" from one to ten times a day, always going for the peak experience. The person is in a continuous state of hyper-excitement, unable to eat or sleep. When the user decides to terminate this "speed binge" the reasons usually include exhaustion and fatigue, abnormal psychological circumstances that are frightening, or inability to obtain the drug. Once the "run" (speed binge) is terminated we then see the reaction phase of the cycle. The reaction phase to the "speed binge" is classically the exhaustion syndrome. The individual often lapses into a deep sleep for periods of from 24 to 48 hours, depending on the duration of the "speed binge"; and upon awakening may eat ravenously.

Unfortunately, many of the methamphetamine users do not return to a baseline level of personality function. They have a prolonged subacute phase in which profound depression dominates. Very often the addict will use "crank" again to treat the depression and another cycle begins. Very rapidly, a situation of desperation develops in which the addict sees no hope for interruption of this pattern of drug use, and the only feasible therapy is to remove the individual from that drug-using subculture.

Patients coming into treatment may exhibit only a predominance of psychological consequences, especially if they have a family and are employed. The five primary categories of distress can be divided into the following: (1) anxiety reaction, (2) amphetamine psychosis, (3) exhaustion syndrome, (4) prolonged depression, (5) prolonged hallucinosis.

The major psychological complaint encountered was the acute anxiety reaction. The individual had overdosed and had become acutely anxious, concerned, and trembling, often with tachycardia. The psychosis is associated with three diagnostic characteristics: (1) visual, (2) auditory hallucinations, and (3) a well-defined system of paranoia.

QUESTION

"How long does amphetamine and methamphetamine remain in the urine?"

Amphetamine and Methamphetamine can be detected in urine approximately two to four days following use. With larger doses and with a diet that produces an alkaline urine, it is possible to obtain positive results for up to seven to nine days. Of course, cases can always be found to contradict these approximations."[1]

"Will drinking vinegar in any amount cause a false negative result?

Drinking vinegar can cause a more rapid elimination of certain drugs (e.g. methamphetamine, amphetamine, PCP). However, the amount required and the degree of control needed to achieve a negative test result is probably beyond most people."[1]

Hell Carried On—I

Paul graduated from college and started working in the business world. He was quite outgoing and did excellent work. His wife, Sandi, was lovely. Their son was a frequent playmate of my son. Our friendship chilled when I confronted him about his first love. You see, supporting a family and a mistress takes some doing. Paul's other lady was cocaine.

Paul didn't sleep very well because he knew an ounce of coke was hidden in his Corvette. He was hungry, but not for food. The cocaine was to be divided up at work. Paul left for work but parked nearby so that he could see when his wife left to go to her job. Once she was off, he was back in the neighborhood, triggered his garage door opener and disappeared into his home.

He activated the burglar alarm. He snorted an estimated one-half gram before phoning in sick. It was hard to punch in the numbers because he was shaky. He closed all the mini blinds and sat at a table upstairs facing the street. His daughter's make-up mirror, a collection of measuring spoons, a 7–11 straw and razor blade completed the set up. The coke was already there. It wasn't even nine in the morning and he had finished a gram. He started to sweat so a headband became part of his attire.

Paul liked looking down the street because he could see anybody who drove by. He double-checked that the phone recorder was turned on. When he went to the bathroom to wipe the sweat off his chest, he noticed the Dial soap had some dirt pressed into the recessed letters. Using his toothbrush, Paul got the bar of soap beautifully clean. Additionally, he cleaned the sink and polished the fixtures. He scrubbed the toilet bowl, the bath tub and floor. He could concentrate, but not for long on any single task. Paul snorted another one-half gram of coke.

As the noise of cars coming down the street increased towards noon, he became increasingly frightened that someone might stop by. He had to watch all the time. He heard car doors close and knew some of his friends might be coming by during lunch. Paul did some more coke.

He couldn't leave the window and was standing up so he could see all the way down to the corner. He started to clean up the mirror, but as soon as it got clean, he used it again and licked off the remaining cocaine powder. He was unable to make any decision. He was totally absorbed in fear and anxiety. The garage door opened. Someone drove in. He hid everything, but not the Corvette. And the burglar alarm was turned on from inside. His wife entered the house and deactivated the alarm.

"Honey, where are you?" Paul and his wife had a king-sized bed with a medium sized drawer below the mattress. He hid in the drawer. Approximately 45 minutes later she found him—a sweaty, paranoid mess. At Paul's request, she drove to the store and purchased a couple of six packs of beer. He had agreed to go to the hospital in exchange for the beer. He needed something to come down. Before she got back, Paul did another gram and then hid the rest in the yard. Paul did get detoxed, and after finally getting home discovered he was quite hungry.

The Paranoid Schizophrenic Reaction

The paranoid schizophrenic cannot filter out the sensations that are received. The normal individual can do so. As the latter listens to a speaker, any disturbing or distracting inputs are screened out, ignored, or put into a secondary state. The toxic cocaine user who listens to a speaker may not be able to do this. Various stimuli may be perceived with equal intensity. The ticking of a clock, a siren in the distance, the sounds coming from a television program may be integrated into the speech that is being heard. The sirens may sound like they are coming to where you are, the noise of a car door closing may seem like it's directly in front of your house. In reality the car is parked down the street. Such interpretations are the basis for the paranoid reactions of the chronic cocaine user.

The "attention deficit" results in one thought being fused into the next in the mind of the toxic cocaine addict. The inability to distinguish and interpret between various stimuli is typical of the disordered sense perceptions of the mind. Cocaine addiction is a primary disease in itself. Like alcoholism, its causes are multifactorial.

QUESTIONNAIRE

Dr. Mark Gold developed the following questionnaire on whether or not a person has a cocaine problem:

1. Do you use cocaine two or more times a week?
2. Would you use more if you could afford it?
3. Do you use whatever cocaine you have continuously until you run out?
4. Are you worried that if you stop using cocaine your work will suffer or you'll lose motivation and enthusiasm?
5. Do you experience a mild anticipation high just knowing you are about to use cocaine?
6. Do you use cocaine alone?
7. Have you ever pilfered money from a joint account to buy cocaine?
8. Do you downplay your coke use to avoid repercussions at home or at work?
9. Do you feel uncomfortable when you read an article or see something on TV about cocaine?
10. Do you do cocaine in your car, in the bathroom, at work, on airplanes or in other public places?
11. Do you feel cocaine helps you overcome shyness or depression?

12. Do you see less of your non-using friends than before, and do you spend time with people you wouldn't be around if it weren't for cocaine?
13. Do you miss work, reschedule appointments or fail to meet family obligations because of cocaine?

14. Do you suffer withdrawal symptoms, either physical or psychological, when you don't have cocaine available?
15. Have people said that you have changed since you began using cocaine?

Yes to any one of the questions is a warning that you may be an addict.
Yes to any two means that the chances are that you are an addict.
Yes to three or more means you are definitely an addict.

Adapted from "1–800-COCAINE"

Some can answer without hesitation. Others aren't so sure. Twelve step programs, such as Cocaine Anonymous, believe that no one can decide for another whether he or she is addicted. One thing is sure, every single member has denied being an addict, sometimes for months, for years, or until death. It is possible for an addict to sincerely believe that he or she was in control, when in fact cocaine was the master.

Summary

Cocaine abuse throughout the world has reached epidemic proportions. Primary and secondary drug addiction is a problem that cannot be controlled by counseling and psychotherapy. Far broader and more intensive efforts are needed. It will not be controlled by isolated effort or by limited attention. Education is an important part of society's effort to prevent the undesirable effects of drug abuse. Knowledge of drugs and their multiple consequences can make only a partial contribution to the solving of this problem. Dishonesty begins with a pattern of unnecessary little lies and deceits with family, friends and co-workers. Then comes the important lies to yourself. It's called denial, to devise plausible explanations for one's acts, usually in self-deception. Solutions lie within the individual.

Cocaine is a stimulant agent that can produce an excited emotional state and occasional euphoria. Further, for some individuals who feel profoundly depressed by an overwhelming world, cocaine can fleetingly make the unbearable seem bearable. These properties can lead to the highest degree of psychic dependence. True tolerance is uncertain, and an "opiate" type of physical dependence does not develop, yet a profound and potentially dangerous type of drug abuse may ensue.

The median age in 12 step recovery programs hovers around the mid-twenties. Most of these younger adults admit to the use of other substances in addition to cocaine, alcohol being the most prevalent.

Self-Test

1. Which soft drink company takes the cocaine out of the imported leaves and turns it over to the government for medical use? (A) Pepsi; (B) Dr. Pepper; (C) Coca-Cola; (D) Minute Maid Orange.

2. Street chemists discovered a way to lower the melting point of cocaine so it could be efficiently heated, vaporized and smoked. This product is known as: (A) Methadone; (B) LAAM; (C) Fentanyl; (D) Crack.

3. MDMA is a designer drug containing derivatives of: (A) peyote and codeine; (B) amphetamine and a hallucinogen; (C) heroin and LSD; (D) phencyclidine and crack.

4. Identify the correct statement: (A) injected cocaine takes fifteen to thirty seconds to reach the brain; (B) the fastest route, about eight seconds, is smoking either freebase or crack; (C) when absorbed through the gum or snorted, the onset of action is three to five minutes; (D) all of the foregoing.

5. Which statement best describes the Kindling Effect? (A) the addict will relapse faster and harder; (B) autopsies on the heart of cocaine addicts showed a high incidence of permanent contraction in the muscle fibers; (C) damaging effects from the use of cocaine during the decade of the 1970's are now appearing in epidemic proportions; (D) an imbalance of the neurotransmitters in the brain.

6. Can any medication other than cocaine cause a positive cocaine test result? (A) absolutely not; (B) antihistamines; (C) PPA; (D) Methamphetamine.

7. Identify the hottest selling drug in blue collar areas: (A) Crystal Meth; (B) Crank; (C) Methamphetamine; (D) all of the foregoing.

8. Select the correct statement: (A) one "line' of street coke weighs between 5–10 mg., and contains around 500 mg., cocaine if the material at hand were 50 percent purity; (B) "Basing" usually involves a single dosage; (C) one 1/15 of a gram contains about 67 mg. cocaine in the form of crack; (D) a "tenth" would be 100 mg. of preprocessed cocaine; (E) all of the foregoing.

Answers: 1(C); 2(D); 3(B); 4(D); 5(A); 6(A); 7(D); 8(E)

113

Notes

1. "Reprinted from the PharmChem Newsletter c. 1988, PharmChem Laboratories, Inc., by permission."

Bibliography

1. Washton, Arnold. *Cocaine Addiction.* 243 pp. W.W. Norton and Co., New York, New York, 1989.
2. Baum, J., *One Step Over The Line.* Harper and Row, San Francisco, California, 1985.
3. Schilnick, Lawrence. *The Coke Book.* 233pp. Berkeley Books, New York, New York, 1984.
4. Gold, Mark S., M.D. *800-Cocaine.* 98pp. Bantam, New York, New York, 1984.

CHAPTER SEVEN

Tactics For Stopping Cocaine

Introduction

The simplest solution of all, if it can be achieved, is not to start using drugs of any kind. The greatest pressure to smoke, drink, and use cocaine or methamphetamine will come from friends or acquaintances. None of these people can force you to use drugs if your mind is made up to leave them alone. Refusing offers of any kind of drug will represent your own decision to maintain your freedom of choice. If you don't have a problem, why start one?

Addiction is defined as compulsion, loss of control and continued use in spite of adverse consequences. Cocaine belongs to the family of addictive diseases. The amphetamine addict is described as a person who dislikes himself and is driven by a compulsive urge to use stimulating drugs to achieve something better. Crystal Meth is one of the methamphetamines needing special attention because it is particularly harmful when abused and because more and more young people seem to be turning to it. A compulsive drug-using lifestyle appears to be developing among the crystal users.

The methamphetamine user is likely to act in a destructive way toward others especially when combining this drug with alcohol. In animal experiments it was found that the drug toxicity increased when animals were brought together; one animal would kill another in hyperexcited and agitated states. With humans, the destructive social effects of methamphetamine abuse have not been fully revealed, but it is already apparent that the "crank," or methamphetamine using community has violent characteristics.

Until recently, cocaine has been a rare drug. Even today, when it is relatively plentiful, it is often diluted by a variety of substance combinations. In this chapter, an attempt is made to outline various drug combinations and their particular problems and offer practical advise to be followed if the street stimulant addict has an honest desire to stop using the drug, permanently.

Hell Carried On—II

Paul started his car and took off. It wasn't safe at home anymore. His wife and son thought he was cured. He really did want to stop, yet still felt he could control the drug. Paul attempted to return to recreational use. His two previous attempts to stop had failed. At the urging of his wife Paul had entered a hospital-based treatment program. He stayed 22 days. Paul entered rehabilitation medically stable and emotionally unstable. He left the same way. He read one book while in treatment. "The Silence of the Lambs," a book of fiction. He liked the following line.

_____ QUOTATION _____
"It's not what happened, I happened."
Hannibal Lector M.D., fictional
character created by Thomas Harris.
_____

Paul was not responding to treatment. He had already thrown over $100,000 down this sewer. His dealer had the signed pink slip for his Corvette. When he was released from treatment, Paul's case worker said he was "gravely concerned," about his future and recommended a recovery home.

His wife was beautiful, devoted and supportive. She was better than a recovery home. Besides he had to go back to work.

Paul started drinking more heavily. He seemed uneasy and was difficult to approach. One weekday he phoned his dealer. He was curious if his dealer had sold his Corvette. He wanted it back and the credit union would handle the financing.

They got to talking about the hospital program, how things were going at work and at home. But business is business, they had to negotiate a price for the car. His dealer had been unable to sell the car. Paul started feeling tense when he could see that his dealer would not sell the car for less than what was owed.

Paul's dealer recently bought a pound of cocaine for $12,000.00. That's what he said. The bait was on the hook. He would throw in a couple of ounces for a cash payment. The credit union made Paul a personal loan. He had the cash. Paul wanted the Corvette back. His VW Bug found the connection's house.

The dealer manipulated Paul for a $1,500.00 discount on an overpriced car. Paul figured this arrangement to be a good deal, $750.00 an ounce and his Corvette. Business was completed. Before he left, Paul expressed a desire to use. Out came the oval mirror, a razor blade, straw and the cocaine. He didn't overdo it, just about three quarters of a gram. It was safe there, he liked the taste and smell and numbness when he licked the mirror. He added a little baking soda. It made smoking fun.

It was dark when he left. Paul was quite hot. He rolled down the windows. He was headed for a motel but the lights from other cars really bothered him. About every third or forth stop sign, he took the turnoff and found a place to park. If he could determine that he wasn't being followed, he could use more cocaine. Paul made numerous stops, purchased two cases of beer, and after hours of driving arrived at a motel about 10 miles from home.

February nights often are in the 30's, so the clerk must have thought it odd to see such heavy perspiration on a guy in a t—shirt. Paul had no choice. He was too shaky to handle money or write a check so payment was made by a credit card. He would pay it off before his wife could see the invoice. It was hard to sign the slip. He got the room key, went to his car and got both cases of beer. He drank some beer and returned for the coke, tightly sealed in that zip-lock bag. *This will last a long time, he thought.*

Back in the room he used more cocaine and drank several beers. His nose was almost totally swollen shut, but he could still snort some of the finely chopped coke. The rocks would fall out of his nose. He started eating them.

Paul was worried about the maid service at 9:30 AM. He started to look out the peep hole in the motel door. The "Do Not Disturb" sign hung on the door. He spent most of the time looking out the door, in an acute state of fear, hearing movements nearby. His back was getting stiff. The paranoia was worse, he could hardly walk. If he could just get straight. He was so hot. If he could just leave it alone. He started eating it, sticking his tongue in the bag. Paul was trapped, his body wrapped in a bed sheet. It was soaking wet. He soaked his body in a cold water bath and ate cocaine from a teaspoon. Icing his head felt the best. Paul had a history of seeing secret tunnels opening up in the walls, he got terrible hallucinations. "I get as paranoid as you could possibly get, and yet, I wouldn't refuse coke."

When his wife received a phone call one day later, he was dead. The sheet had been torn into strips, braided into a rope and fastened to a ventilation duct in the ceiling. *The enemy had won.*

Treatment Considerations

Predictably, many cocaine users experience depression and mood swings during the first week of treatment. Generally, after the cocaine is gone the user experiences a "crash." Depression, slowed motor response, and decreased sexual drive all contribute to the impression that cocaine use, by comparison, is preferable to living without. This is a time of high risk for the person who is abstinent.

Empathy is crucial in the recovery process of the addict. It is the ability to understand another so completely that the feelings, thoughts, and reasoning of the other are readily comprehended. This does not mean that all of the patient's desires or needs are fulfilled. There is a difference between the coke addict and the alcoholic which needs to be understood. The cocaine addict generally is seen as grandiose and often condescending in his or her attitude. The alcoholic more often is observed to be depressed, resentful, and a passive victim.

A preliminary study by psychiatrists at the University of Minnesota School of Medicine in Minneapolis showed that carbamazine, a drug used to prevent seizures and treat certain forms of depression, can help control cocaine cravings well enough for addicts to benefit from more traditional forms of treatment. This is the first drug where preliminary evidence suggests a significant level of reduction in cocaine craving.

_____ QUOTATION_____

"Cocaine treatment fails because patients are trapped by craving. We feel that we may have found (a drug) . . . that cures or eliminates craving."

Dr. James Halikas, co-director of the chemical
dependency treatment program at the University
of Minnesota and director of the study.

Note: Carbamazepine is the generic term for Tegretol, one of the principle medicines used to treat epilepsy. An estimated 4.9 million Americans are afflicted. Women who took Tegretol during pregnancy were more likely to produce babies with delayed development and mental retardation. The New England Journal of Medicine in June 1989., Ed.

What is PPA?

Phenylpropanolamine (PPA) is a synthetic stimulant found in over-the-counter (OTC) preparations for colds and weight control. OTC products containing PPA include Alka-Seltzer Plus, Allerest, Contact, Coricidin, Dexatrim, Sucrets, Sinutab, and Vicks Formula 44 D, to name only a few. These and other OTC drugs will NOT be reported as positive for the illicit drugs amphetamine or methamphetamine.[1]

PPA has been implicated in hundreds of reports, many of them emphasizing the feelings of nervousness, anxiety and irritability that overcome some people who take pills containing the ingredient. Medications containing PPA used to be sold on the street as substitutes for amphetamines or "speed".

Use of Drug Combinations

David E. Smith, M.D. published an article on "Cocaine-Alcohol Abuse: Epidemiological, Diagnostic and Treatment Considerations" in the *Journal of Psychoactive Drugs,* which provided a partial source to medical intricacies.

Sobriety is the initial goal and that means being free from all substances. There is a great potential for the cocaine user to be addicted to several other substances such as alcohol and marijuana as well. About 90 percent also reported alcohol use. Over half reported marijuana use of two or more times a week. Cocaine Anonymous meetings are considered essential for any recovering person. People don't become addicted in a vacuum; nor do they become clean and sober by themselves.

Cocaine users are susceptible to the upper-downer syndrome associated with amphetamines, which share many effects but without the glamorous reputation. To control cocaine's antagonistic stimulant-depressant effects, users commonly combine the drug with alcohol. This pattern can contribute to acute intoxication, which in turn may precipitate drunk driving accidents as well as chronic alcohol abuse.

The use of alcohol or other depressants, such as marijuana or tranquilizers, to relieve cocaine's effects can become a secondary drug pattern. When people with multiple drug problems seek treatment, they often turn to alcohol treatment centers where they may encounter both inadequate information and mixed attitudes toward multiple drug addiction. Therefore, the cocaine-alcohol abuser poses a problem for traditional alcohol recovery programs.

The high-dose cocaine abuser may also use opiates, such as heroin or other controlled drugs. The substantial increase in the smoking of cocaine free base is associated with a parallel increase in the smoking of Persian heroin. Individuals using this combination are primarily cocaine abusers who have escalated their dosage. Initially they smoke the heroin as an opiate downer to calm the stimulant side effects of cocaine. However, they may acquire narcotic hunger and a desire for heroin and thereby evolve into primary heroin users or heroin-cocaine addicts.

Complications

A massive overdose of cocaine can produce seizures and cardiac arrhythmia. Intravenous Valium and support of the cardiorespiratory system are appropriate. Hypertensive crisis must be controlled with medication. Medical care is imperative. Overdosage with street stimulants is apt to cause disorganized behavior, inability to sleep, paranoid ideas which may lead to violent acts, hallucinations and other symptoms. Withdrawal may produce psychiatric problems such as depression and fatigue. There's a tremendous variability between different people, and in the same person at different times. A person who ingests too much coke would be extremely nervous, flighty, have problems concentrating and inability to sleep.

Chronic use can produce paranoia or pseudo-hallucinations. These hallucinations may be visual or auditory. Many people run the risk of paranoid schizophrenic reactions because the paranoia keeps them from going to the emergency room. *Hospitals don't report drug toxicity to the police.* In the amphetamine psychosis the major treatment is antipsychotic drugs of the *phenothiazine* (stelazine, thorazine or malarial) type. *Haldol* is a very effective prescription used to treat psychotic reactions, and is the drug of choice in many drug detox facilities.

In this mental state, people will often self-medicate themselves. Alcohol is probably taken most frequently, pot will suffice as will any of the tranquilizers. If high quantities of stimulants are used, odds favor that depressants will follow.

The acute anxiety reaction or the "overamp" toxic effect described by cocaine abusers usually can be managed in an outpatient setting with reassurance, a supportive environment and oral sedative-hypnotic medication, such as Valium. Medical supervision is essential.

Similar to amphetamines, prolonged high-dose (one to four grams a day) administration of cocaine is associated with sleep deprivation, psychosis with auditory and visual hallucinations, and paranoia. It is possible to manage these cocaine psychoses with the use of *haloperidol.* If this medication does not work, hospitalization in a psychiatric unit and higher doses of haloperidol are indicated.

If the cocaine addict has been using benzodiazepines (tranquilizers) on a continual basis to calm down, the withdrawal is more complicated. For example, the combination of cocaine and Valium is most likely to produce a seizure after about six days of abstinence. Cocaine and Ativan peaks out on about the second day. Cocaine and alcohol reaches its highest seizure potential about the ninth day. A personal history of seizure disorders must be treated by the physician to minimize life threatening withdrawal complications.

When individuals speedball (inject heroin and cocaine simultaneously in order to combine the intense euphoria of cocaine with the anxiety-free sensation of the opiate), the risk of acute overdose reactions increases, either because of the stimulant or depressant effect.

Treatment And Recovery

There is a substantial withdrawal phenomenon from cocaine addiction, characterized by difficulty in sleeping and a strong desire to return to the use of cocaine, although if cocaine is used alone there are generally no life threatening withdrawal problems caused by the drug.

> "One of the big problems in stopping the use of cocaine (or any other addictive drug), even after the body is free from it, is the role the drug plays in a person's emotional life. Your body may no longer need the drug, but that doesn't mean you don't want it."
>
> Paul Erlich, program director of the Forest Farm Community, a Marin County drug treatment clinic.

Medical treatment theory may include the prescription of tricyclic-antidepressants. It is generally recommended to wait one month before making a decision to start medication. The antidepressants help build up depleted neurotransmitters. Extensive nutritional supplements aid restoration after neurotransmitter depletion.

David Smith, M.D., and Donald Wesson, M.D., co-authored the book *Treating Cocaine Dependency*, which suggests specific doses of both amino acids and prescription medications. Tyrosine is an over the counter amino acid and has been discussed previously. Amantadine, Desipramine and Bromocriptine are all prescription medications which may be of value. Dosage of these medications should be determined by a qualified physician.

Clinical experience with individuals who are cocaine abusers indicates that over 90 percent have a primary addictive disease without major mental disorders. For those with major underlying emotional disorders, such as endogenous depression (caused by factors within the person), antidepressants in conjunction with problem-oriented counseling and participation in a recovery group is usually the treatment of choice. This is best accomplished through a combination of individual and group therapy provided in an outpatient setting. Principles of recovery and constructive alternatives as a way of dealing with cocaine hunger should be stressed. The recovery process requires substantial education of the addict on addictive disease generally and cocaine specifically. Supportive family members and friends are needed for this process to succeed.

Truth And Reality

Both the cocaine addict and alcoholic are in touch with reality. Their values will be distorted, and reality will be seen through a self-fulfilling fog. Nevertheless, neither is totally oblivious to life. The addict's perception of life may be very distorted, and misjudgments border on being insane. The major difference is that the addict's and alcoholic's accounts sound logical. Be careful, when the addict's story seems reasonable, you are probably being taken.

121

No treatment center of any quality would ever say that the cocaine addict is not responsible for sobriety and entry into recovery. Treatment counselors tell patients, after therapy, "You now have a choice. The drug is out of your system. You understand the disease. You know how to get help and where to go for it. Even if you have a relapse, you know it's part of the disease and you can still recover and stay that way. There is hope."

Unfortunately, far more cocaine addicts relapse and suffer consequences of the disease, than those who get sober and well. *One Line is too Much and 100 is not Enough* .

The addicted person may be so convincing that lies become truth. The addict may get family, friends and employer to believe his or her version of things. The addict is in complete denial which prevents any change. It is crucial to involve the entire family in the treatment process because the true state of affairs may not become evident until all observations and experiences are shared. Any session of this nature should be *guided by a professional interventionist.*

Ten Specific Recommendations for Avoiding Relapse

1. *Don't Drink Alcohol.* What is painfully clear is that alcohol (and marijuana) can easily trigger the desire to use cocaine again, often combined with impaired judgment that controlled use is a genuine alternative. Alcohol is closely associated with cocaine in most people's minds. Many people feel that since their primary problem was cocaine and they never had a problem with alcohol or marijuana, that as long as they avoid cocaine they can continue to use their secondary drugs of choice. Clinical research shows that 93 percent of cocaine addicts who drink will use coke again. A drug-free philosophy must be stressed as a treatment goal.

2. *Open Up.* Silence is the enemy of recovery. Tell your family and friends that you are quitting. Open discussions supplemented with positive alternatives are necessary to prevent reuse and relapse. Often your family already knows there is a problem but doesn't know what it is. Family members will support you, whenever possible. They may provide financial help if you need to go into treatment. It is vitally important to know that living a comfortable and responsible life without the use of drugs is possible and can be a very positive, life enhancing process. The term "cure" in the sense that the individual can return to controlled cocaine use, has no place in an effective recovery program.

3. *Limit Conversations About Cocaine.* This is a very important strategy. During the recovery period, addictive thinking, cocaine hunger, and cue identification are critical. Drug hunger will predate the first reuse of cocaine, and first reuse most always leads to relapse. When you talk

with your dealer, your "automatic thought" will be to buy. Besides your dealer is a salesman whose job is to contact prospective buyers. Dealers are generally friendly, your money finances their lives. If you believe you have a friend who deals, try not paying your drug debt. Watch his or her personality change. Threats will follow.

If you're engaged in a cocaine discussion, it will more than likely lead to "euphoric recall." Movies and songs about cocaine will have the same effect. You have a compulsive craving for cocaine. Your pulse rate has gone up, and you haven't used the drug. Conversations about cocaine are the biggest reason for most people's failure to follow through on their decision to quit using. Don't expose yourself to avoidable threats. Focus on recovery fundamentals.

4. *Eliminate Tempting Stimuli.* The first 30-days should focus on the discontinuance of all unnecessary psychoactive drug use. Abstinence training, drug education (that includes the family), and pragmatic tasks, such as discarding drug paraphernalia and breaking off drug-related acquaintances are a priority. Any scales, "cutting agents", pipes, jars and papers containing cocaine (bindles) must be discarded. The more intimately associated the place or thing is with cocaine, the more important it is to get rid it. If you carry a wallet that was used for storage of cocaine, buy a new and different one. Every time you open the change pouch, you will initially explore for an overlooked gram of cocaine.

5. *Avoid High-Risk Situations.* A recovering cocaine addict needs to combat relapse, which focuses on recognizing the early signs of relapse, such as "euphoric recall," as being very selective and the product of narrow thinking. Avoid high-risk situations and prevent slips from becoming genuine relapses. End relationships that are founded on mutual drug dependence. Permit new drug-free friends and lovers to emerge. Don't try to save anybody, work on salvaging yourself.

The Behavioral Risk Scale ranges from 1 to 10. It can identify risky people, places and things for you. On the scale, 1 is no risk, 10 is relapse and any risk above 5 is too great. For example, ask yourself, would you be in jeopardy if exposed to a relapse-prone environment? If you score too high, don't go. The risk of using cocaine is too great. You can reduce the risk by taking along someone who is a non-user and supportive of your efforts at recovery. If you are away from home, always have your own transportation. Another important strategy is to entertain at home because we have more control than we do when we go to someone else's house. We make the rules in our own homes. Neutral places like restaurants are an easy place to meet. This scale is a mental tool to judge situations. One of the benefits is that it gives you time to consider the situation.

6. *Exercise.* Other important aspects of recovery include an exercise program where the cocaine addict uses exercise not only to improve general health, but also to make recovery a positive process and to deal with cocaine hunger. Exercise that produces cardiopulmonary stimulation in excess of 20 minutes can produce an increase in the release of the body's own endorphins followed by a reduction of anxiety and drug hunger. For cocaine addicts who are used to being artificially stimulated, exercise programs are beneficial.

7. *Beware of Pay Day.* Money is often a cue for a cocaine purchase. Keep your available cash to $20. Give your paycheck to your wife, husband or parents. Permit them to handle your finances until you get back on your feet. Negotiable securities, pink slips and other valuables should be included in this transfer arrangement. Never carry anything with you that will make it easy for you to purchase cocaine. The automatic teller machines are a particular temptation during early recovery. Turn over your cash-generating plastic cards.

8. *Screen Communications.* A common example of communication problems involves telephones and answering machines, because frequently connections are made on the phone. Change your telephone number and install an answering machine. This allows you to screen your calls and gives you control over the calls to which you will respond. Stay in control of your communications. You may want to get an unlisted number, especially if you were a dealer. Cocaine using contacts are very persistent. It is virtually impossible to stop using while still dealing.

9. *Change Your Patterns.* Break up any old habits that are associated with cocaine use. For example, if you take a certain way home from work, going past your dealer's house, find a different way. Otherwise you have a good chance of stopping. If you have a pattern of staying home and isolating yourself that is associated with cocaine use, find ways to get out and be around people who are low-risk company. Identify your own patterns, so you can change them and reduce your risk of using cocaine.

The process of drug hunger (cues) include people, places, things, events and moods. People that should be eliminated are dealers and drug using friends. Places that threaten sobriety are bars and restaurants where you know cocaine is easily accessible, homes where cocaine is available, and even your work situation. You may need to change jobs to recover. Things that act as cues are paraphernalia, mirrors, straws, and other implements. Certain rooms could be redecorated to see them as a different place not connected with cocaine anymore. Events might include concerts, receptions and anniversaries. Travel can be a cue. In self-defeating moods, cocaine may be used as a pick-me-up drug. Happy moods may be cues for those who have been using cocaine as a reward for achievement.

A cue sets off a thought process which becomes part of a drug desire. Drug desire leads to drug hunger. (The person must have a history of drug desire). Without the personal history of drug abuse, the cue is meaningless.

10. *Join Cocaine Anonymous.* Members have a common goal, to stay off of cocaine. You can get all the support you want. Cocaine recovery groups and meetings are the backbone of the recovery process. Recovering cocaine abusers find support groups, such as AA and NA, to be very useful in their recovery, especially given the fact of multiple drug abuse during active cocaine addiction. In the long run, the treatment for cocaine and alcohol addiction looks very similar, with the best recovery rates coming from abstinence and the group process.

Nobody Will Recover For Me

You don't have to know everything about an insult to eliminate the damaging effects, therefore work on: 1) eliminating the drug; 2) finding a support system, and 3) restructuring your life. Find something that will provide more satisfaction than the drug

Summary

The recovery process is lifelong. In the early phases, the cocaine addict is working primarily to achieve relief from guilt and pain created by his or her addiction. However, as recovery progresses there is a movement toward learning to live comfortably and responsibly without the use of cocaine or other drugs. The work will teach you how to do it. Cocaine recovery groups have incorporated the principles of the 12-step programs, coupled with a strong educational component about the characteristics of cocaine addiction. An adult program should focus on rehabilitation, a return to a normal way of life. Most cocaine addicts have enough education to market themselves in mainstream society. Adolescent treatment programs need to focus on "habilitation." Most young people need to be taught new skills so that entry into life may be completed. The maturity of the adolescent drug user was arrested when they became dependent on various drug combinations. Adolescents don't have a strong supportive environment nor have they acquired the skills to compete in life.

Self-Test

1. The cocaine users will most likely: (A) restrict use to that drug alone; (B) combine cocaine and alcohol; (C) mix cocaine and heroin; (D) give up cocaine for alcohol alone; (E) none of the foregoing.

2. Identify the correct statement regarding the cocaine addict: (A) empathy may be crucial in the recovery process of the addict; (B) cocaine treatment fails because patients are trapped by cocaine craving; (C) sobriety is the initial goal and that means being free from all substances; (D) silence is the enemy of recovery; (E) all of the foregoing.

3. It's helpful in resisting a cocaine relapse if you: (A) exercise; (B) carry less cash; (C) change your telephone number; (D) don't drink alcohol; (E) all of the foregoing.

4. The process of drug hunger (cues) includes: (A) drug using friends; (B) concerts, receptions and anniversaries; (C) all types of white powers or resins; (D) travel; (E) all of the foregoing.

5. A massive overdose of cocaine may be a cause of: (A) seizure; (B) irregular beating of the heart; (C) damage to the heart muscles; (D) death; (E) any of the foregoing.

6. Cocaine addiction may be difficult to treat because: (A) the addict may be very convincing in lying about being an addict; (B) families may see no justification for it because they have been deceived; (C) friends may think there is no addiction; (D) professional help may not be available; (E) all of the foregoing.

7. After discontinuance of a combined cocaine-valium addiction, a seizure is most likely to occur about the: (A) 2nd day; (B) 6th day; (C) 9th day; (D) 15th day; (E) 30th day.

8. Select the correct statement: (A) The Behavioral Risk Scale can identify risky people, places and things for you; (B) Cocaine treatment fails because patients are trapped by craving. Your body may no longer need the drug, but that doesn't mean you don't want it. (C) there is a great potential for the cocaine user to be addicted to several other substances as well; (D) it is crucial to involve the entire family in the treatment process because the true state of affairs may not become evident until all observations and experiences are shared; (E) all of the foregoing.

Answers: 1(B); 2(E); 3(E); 4(E); 5(E); 6(E); 7(B); 8(E).

Notes

1. "Reprinted from the PharmChem Newsletter c. 1988, PharmChem Laboratories, Inc., by permission."

Bibliography

1. Vroom, George W. *Are You Missing the Boat to Recovery.* 136 pp. Health Communications Inc., Pompano Beach, Flordia. 1988.
2. Smith, David E., M.D. and Donald R. Wesson, M.D. *Treating Cocaine Dependency. 116 pp. Hazelden Foundation, Center City, Minnesota, 1988.*
3. Weiss, M.D., Roger D. and Steven M. Mirin, M.D. *Cocaine.* 178 pp. Ballantine Books, New York, New York, 1987.
4. O'Connell, Kathleen R. *End Of The Line.* 120pp. The Westminster Press, Philadelphia, Pennsylvania, 1985.
5. *Narcotics Anonymous.* 290 pp. World Service Office, Inc., 16155 Wyandoette Street, Van Nuys, CA 91406, 1984.

CHAPTER EIGHT

The Tranquilizer Controversy

Introduction

Not all drugs are harmful; many have proven value in the treatment of disease. Digitalis for heart failure, antibiotics for bacterial infections, Dilantin for seizure disorders and thousands of other medical drugs can help to alleviate pain, distress and avert death. The widespread use of pharmaceutical drugs is a phenomenon of the twentieth century

The tranquilizers are a group of drugs that relieve tension and anxiety and produce muscular relaxation. Their primary use is for psychiatric reasons. Abuse gives rise to the same symptoms as those from barbiturates abuse. Deaths have been reported from overusage of tranquilizers in combination with other drugs and from barbiturates alone. All of the tranquilizers are capable of producing habituation and addiction. How does a person get into the habit of taking a drug that is not needed for treatment of a disease? There are many routes to addiction. Some people began by continuing to take a drug that had been prescribed for treatment, but which is no longer needed. Drugs are often misused when people are misinformed or when they develop addictive disease by continuing to use the drugs compulsively. Most addicts seek the drugs out in a very sophisticated manner.

Personality and emotions are involved in drug abuse. Tranquilizers have soothed the agitated and belligerent and partially emptied the mental institutions with improvements, if not cures, of patient after patient. Some pill addicts have antisocial personalities and have experienced a wide variety of psychiatric medications. Others are immature, unsure, unstable and overwhelmed. Such a person may see the world as too difficult, too cruel, too frustrating. Such a person may seek to escape behind a "drug curtain". If the mental processes are compromised the person becomes ineffectual.

Americans consume pills at an astonishing rate. More than 2 billion prescriptions are filled at a tremendous financial cost. About twenty percent

129

of the prescriptions are for psychoactive drugs. When these medications are consumed under supervised medical guidance and for appropriate therapeutic purposes they can bring significant benefit to the individual.

May She Sleep in Peace

Wendy was about 22 years old when she first experimented with cocaine. There was never any romance. So much had been said about the drug, both good and bad. She looked for that initial infatuation. It wasn't there. Paranoia, agoraphobia, and fear took over her mind. She became restless and alternating agoraphobia and claustrophobia increased until she was staying first with one friend and then another. Cocaine was no longer in her life. Wendy couldn't handle it. It had handled her.

Fear of riding in cars increased. She could no longer drive on the freeways. Even the smaller roads were becoming a problem. Wendy was frightened to go shopping. She stopped going to the grocery store. Her mother did the shopping. She dropped out of school. Life was hell. She had a nagging fear she was mad.

For the next eight years she hardly ever left her house. Living with her mother was helpful. She started seeing a psychiatrist when she was 28. She was prescribed three different tricyclic antidepressants over months of treatment. Nothing seemed to help. The doctor tried Lithium Carbonate. Again Wendy did not respond. She turned 30. Her doctor prescribed Xanax. Within two days she felt better. Something was different.

At age 32 Wendy completed her university studies and received a degree. She always sat next to the classroom door. Access to a quick exit was comforting. She hired another student to accompany her during all classes. She had a well established escape plan in case of a panic reaction. In effect, she was doing everything necessary to strengthen her self-confidence. She felt comfortable driving so long as she avoided peak commute hours. Her image of herself as a sick person diminished.

Wendy was bright and made continual progress. She continued to take medication, which seemed to be especially effective for her. She may continue taking this drug or a similiar medication for the rest of her life. Is Wendy addicted to Xanax? Of course! *All physicians and patients need to weigh the risks versus the benefits of medical care.* If the risk exceeds the therapeutic value, then treatment must be reconsidered. In Wendy's case, her exposure to cocaine apparently brought out some serious problems that lay just underneath the skin of her personality. Had she never used the drug it is possible that these disorders may not have surfaced.

A Brief History of the Benzodiazepines

When benzodiazepines (tranquilizers) were first marketed, approximately 30 years ago, doctors were told that they were safe and non-addictive. More recent research has disproved this fallacy, and it is well recognized that these drugs are not safe for all consumers. Efforts are continuing to be made to change or challenge medical opinion on this issue.

There is no doubt that tranquilizers, like sedatives, have considerable value in the relief of tensions and anxieties, in the soothing of agitated persons, and in the treatment of certain kinds of psychiatric patients, including some of those who have been committed to mental institutions. The drugs do not make the problems go away, although they can help to keep the patient calm in times of stress. Most people tolerate them well and are able to discontinue medication when they feel better. Unfortunately, many are not so lucky. They can suffer from side-effects, withdrawal reactions, or both.

Thalidomide is the outstanding example of a benzodiazepine drug that was thought to be remarkably safe, but which turned out to be the source of worldwide tragedy. The medication was not used in the United States because it had not been cleared by the Food and Drug Administration. West Germany was the first country to use the drug on a generous scale. Thalidomide became available to other countries, in some of which it could be purchased without a prescription. By the year 1962 medical reports from around the world revealed that thalidomide, when used during pregnancy, could be a cause of badly deformed babies. In West Germany more than 5000 babies were born with gross defects and on a lesser scale the story was repeated in Finland, Brazil, Argentina, Japan, Syria, Africa and England, and wherever the drug was used during pregnancy.

It has become clear that we do not know that much about the biochemistry of the human embryo and that the unborn baby may be damaged by many different drugs. I think it's wise to take the view that any drug taken during pregnancy may possibly injure the unborn. Obviously, if you are required to take medication during pregnancy, discuss it with your doctor and ask to minimize the dose.

Another potential problem for the benzodiazepine consumer is that very few drugs have only the desired therapeutic action. People on tranquilizers often experience side effects. Whether a person experiences side effects or withdrawal symptoms is probably most dependent on how long the drug has been taken (weeks, months, years), the amount of a drug being taken, and physiological make up. Dosages vary according to the specific drug and not necessarily by its weight or amount prescribed. Injectable medication may have a quicker onset and the amount of benzodiazepine received depends on the volume received. For example, an oral dose of 2mg. of Ativan is equivalent to 5 mg. of Valium. One milligram of Xanax will have about the same effect. This is known as the product strength. Drug combinations

131

usually produce a synergism of negative effects. These drugs should not be mixed with alcohol, narcotics, sleeping pills, barbiturates, antihistamines, antidepressants or other tranquilizers.

Take the benzodiazepine as directed, and use it as briefly as possible. Long term use is desirable in certain cases and can do more good than harm, under medical supervision combined with a proper diagnosis. If you have never experienced benzodiazepine withdrawal, hold on tight. *These drugs are the revenge of drug withdrawal.* Many people may be familiar with alcohol withdrawal, some also know about the fatigue and depression coming off coke or crystal methamphetamine. When a person comes off tranquilizers, the pill addict doesn't expect any withdrawal complications. When they are felt, the person is not familiar with what's occurring and can be in an extremely fragile and confused mental state. If the benzodiazepine addict is reducing the dosage at home, the temptation to take a supplemental dose is always there, especially when feeling fragile. Drugs talk to you. They speak in all languages and always say the same thing, "Let's make up honey, I'll be better to you this time, please give me another chance." "I'll make all your pain go away."

People on benzodiazepines often experience some of the following side-effects: depression, agoraphobia, loss of appetite, nausea, dizziness, confusion, poor reading comprehension, impaired thinking and verbal ability, outbursts of rage, lack of coordination, change of personality, minimal tolerance for stress, and feeling emotionally dead.

Unwanted Effects of Psychotropic Drugs

Most treatments, be they surgical or medical in nature, carry risks. Drugs used in treatment have a wide range of adverse effects. There are at least 6 kinds of harmful results that can come from the use of drugs in medical care.

1. A drug may produce too much of a desired result. (For example, if a physician prescribes a tranquilizer to achieve some relief of anxiety and tension it may cause sedation far deeper than intended. Whether or not this excessive reaction results in any harm may depend on the circumstances, as in the possibility of an accident while driving an automobile.)

2. It may not be possible to avoid the undesirable effects of some part of the drug, even though other parts may produce desirable results.

3. Some people taking a prescribed drug may have an allergic (hypersensitive) reaction to it, even though there is no hazard for most patients. Fever, skin rash or a drop in cardiac output (exces-

sively low blood pressure) may occur in addition to destructive effects on the blood.

4. Reactions may occur to drugs because of a genetic (hereditary) predisposition to addictive disease or some other factor. Severe behavioral changes, an inability to predict immediate future behavior or a seizure may be an example of such a condition.

5. Some drugs may reactivate a dormant or intermittent illness. For example, caution must be taken when prescribing any psychoactive or opiate medication to a recovering alcoholic or drug addict who has ceased the use of a drug. The medication may be prescribed properly, but may trigger a memory of prior use. The drug may talk to you, "Hey, Jaime remember me? I miss you and love you". Psychological dependence has opened the door to addiction again. You don't have to walk through.

6. Drugs may interact with other drugs in the body to produce unexpected consequences. An enormous number of such reactions are already known and new ones are constantly being discovered. Some studies have found that nearly 20 per cent of all undesirable effects of drugs are due to interactions. One substance may interfere with the actions of another, may combine to cause ill effects, may complicate treatment for another illness, may accentuate or magnify results (a synergistic effect) and in general increase the chances of a toxic reaction in various ways.

In general, the very young and the very old are more susceptible to complications from drugs. Persons with an allergic history are also more likely to be affected adversely than others. The taking of a multiple number of drugs is especially apt to be associated with unforseen reactions. *Sedatives hypnotics and minor tranquilizers* may accentuate the depressant effects of each other and the latter may be further emphasized if phenothiazines, alcohol, or antihistamines are taken. These drugs are all hazardous because they may alter the metabolism of other drugs as well as having their own depressant effects.

Proper care calls for hospitalization that gives support to respiration, and treatment for possible medical problems such as pneumonia or shock. Patients seldom tell the truth about the extent of their pill taking. The person may not know. The problem is that rapid removal from the drug may lead to serious withdrawal difficulities. Graded reduction minimizes withdrawal complications. Never stop abruptly.

Not to be overlooked is the strong tendency of some patients to have side effects unrelated to the drug that was being consumed. In other words, psychological expectations may produce anticipatory symptoms that could not possibly be associated with drug withdrawal. In short, the person is afraid to stop taking the medication. Reactions of this nature may be attention-seeking in nature, may be due to hysteria, the power of suggestion or some other cause unrelated to the treatment being given.

It is not uncommon for pill addicts to seek out a doctor who can be influenced by the skilled patient into writing a prescription for a phantom disorder. Patients can work several doctors concurrently and may addict themselves. Prescription-refill authorization can be made by bold and desperate patients, and there are numerous illegal means to obtain prescription drugs. Suddenly, the patient has a problem and the doctor is being questioned by the local pharmaceutical consortium. Is the doctor creating illness by liberally dispensing medication? Is this iatrogenic illness (caused by the doctor) or has the patient manipulated doctors, pharmacists, people and the medicine cabinets?

A Potential Health Hazard

The following drugs represent a partial listing of commonly prescribed sedative-hypnotic compounds known as the Benzodiazepines. The commonly known names of these products follow.

1. Alprazolam *	9. Halcion*	17. Prazepam
2. Ativan *	10. Halazepam	18. Paxipam
3. Buspar	11. Librax	19. Restoril *
4. Clorazepate	12. Librium	20. Serax *
5. Centrax	13. Meprobamate	21. Temazepam *
6. Clonipin	14. Midazolam *	22. Tranxene
7. Dalmane	15. Mogadon (Canada, Europe)	23. Valium
8. Flurazepam	16. Oxazepam *	24. Xanax *

The list introduced to you may look long, however try to keep in mind that there are approximately 800 different tranquilizers on the world market in 1990. The asterisk identifying certain drugs indicates that these benzodiazepines have a shorter half-life and the symptoms may appear quickly. Anyone coming off these types of drugs should be tapered, by taking diminishing doses. A physician should supervise the withdrawal. Remember, *physical dependence is a syndrome of predictable physical symptoms which appear when someone stops using a drug suddenly.* Benzodiazepine withdrawal for heavy, long term users is more medically complicated than coming off alcohol, heroin, or cocaine. That little pill has got an incredible kick to it, which is most apparent when the medication is stopped.

Drugs UNMARKED with an asterisk have a long half-life, including Mogadon for our friends in Canada and in Europe. Delay in the appearance of withdrawal symptoms is due to the prolonged life of these drugs and their metabolities. The appearance of withdrawal symptoms is not a black and white issue. Despite the discussion of side effects or undesirable reactions, they do not occur at all in many patients. Some persons must be exposed to drugs for months to years before unwanted effects occur.

The benzodiazepines are referred to as the minor tranquilizers because they are used to treat the more minor emotional or psychiatric disorders. The half-life of these drugs is less than those of the phenothiazines.

The phenothiazines are the so-called major tranquilizers, which implies a stronger drug. However they are really called major because of their use in severe psychiatric illnesses. Stelazine, Thorazine and Melaril all have a longer half-life. Once the effective dose is reached, the patient will be aware they are under the effect of the medication. For example, Thorazine may be given to a violent person, for protective reasons.

Benzodiazepine, a chemical widely used and abused in our society is used primarily by mainstream society. It is sold legally and also can be obtained on the street. The drug is not a drug of abuse in the "drug culture" other than to calm major drug withdrawal.

The following paragraphs will be directed to the everyday user of Benzodiazepine drugs so that the benefits and consequences of prescribed usage can be better understood.

Benzodiazepines are insidious and deceptive in producing increased tolerance and subsequent dependency. Rarely does a person see problems with Valium until it is discontinued or unless mixed with another sedative agent, such as alcohol. When used in moderate dosage (15–20 mg/d) for a short period of time (5–7days), Diazepam is judged to be a safe and effective drug. It is often used for the treatment of tension, anxiety, muscle spasms, psychoneurosis, skin rashes, alcohol withdrawal, alcoholism, insomnia, agitation, hallucinations, and convulsions. In fact, Valium has been used for almost all body complaints known to the human race. Valium has been reclassified in certain states and is generally accepted as being an addictive drug. Usage of diazepam in excess of five to seven days is discouraged. It is not considered safe. Any sedative-hypnotic drug is addictive.

Valium has been on the market for awhile and the pharmaceutical firm will be manufacturing these pills in white, (Roche 2); yellow, (Roche 5); and the blue, (Roche 10); until its 17 year patent runs out. The yellow ones are five milligrams each. All drugs have the same potential for trouble. Some have greater dependency potentials than others, however. Tranquilizers and barbiturates have the greatest potential for severe and dangerous withdrawal reactions. Some 10 percent get hooked at clinically recommended doses. Valium has no minimum lethal dose when taken alone. Just don't drink alcohol while taking these pills. According to the Drug Abuse Warning Network (DAWN), the most common drug a senior citizen took in a drug related suicide was *Valium taken with alcohol.*

List of Benzodiazepines Available	Dose (mg) Equivalent to 10 mg. Valium
Chlordiazepoxide (Librium)	25 mg.
Diazepam (Valium)	10 mg.
Lorazapam (Ativan)	1–2 mg.
Nitrazepam (Mogadon)	10 mg.
Oxazepam (Serenid)	20 mg.
Temazepam (Normison, Euhypnos)	20 mg.
Triazolam (Halcion)	0.5 mg.

The Controlled Substance Act of 1970 classified drugs into five schedules. The state of New York recently reclassified Valium, moving it from among the schedule IV drugs to a schedule ll drug. Morphine Sulphate, Dilaudid and Demerol all have a high potential for addiction as does Valium.

Research on the dependence-inducing properties of benzodiazepines has been well-documented. All of these agents can cause withdrawal reactions. Escalation of dosage and tell-tale signs of drug seeking behavior have been reported.

Psychoactive Metabolities

The longer an active drug is in the body, the longer the good effects and bad effects will continue. To increase drug effectiveness, pharmacologists have been able to design drugs which can delay metabolism and excretion. For example, the action of liver enzymes on some Benzodiazepines (Valium and Librium included), instead of deactivating them, transform them into other active metabolites. The psychoactive metabolite of Valium is named des-methyldiazepam. This metabolite and others extend the medication's life span in your body. Delay in the appearance of withdrawal symptoms is due to the prolonged life of this drug and its metabolities. Valium is fat soluble. The liver metabolizes all of the Benzodiazepines. The abuse of alcohol in the past may affect how rapidly the metabolities are eliminated. Age is also a big factor. Tolerance for these drugs tends to diminish with increasing age. Susceptibility increases as tolerance declines. Any undesirable effect can be exaggerated.

Although the various benzodiazepines are generally equivalent in treatment of anxiety, the differences in active metabolities and duration of activity may have an effect on the withdrawal symptoms. The longer acting agents (i.e., Valium, Tranxene, Centrax) may offer a tapering effect, minimizing some withdrawal symptoms. There seems to be a general consensus that benzodiazepines should not be withdrawn abruptly but rather tapered off after prolonged use. The graduated reduction should not exceed 10 percent per day.

Tagamet and Antabuse have been reported to reduce the elimination of benzodiazepines, therefore prolonging the half-life of these long-acting agents. The interaction does not seem to occur with Ativan and Serax. A recent New England Journal of Medicine article reports that oral contraceptives may also increase the half-life of Valium. These interactions may all contribute to increased sedation and impaired coordination.

The elderly are significantly more likely to exhibit central nervous system depressant side effects. Age related changes such as decreased metabolism and excretion results in accumulation of the benzodiazepines. The half-life of Valium in an elderly person may be two to three times that of a young adult. Elderly people taking benzodiazepines exhibit more confusion often mislabeled as senility.

What is a Half-Life?

The half-life is the amount of time needed for one half of any drug or other substance to disappear from the body because of excretion, transformation into a different chemical, simple decay, or other processes.

The half-life for the benzodiazepine drugs varies according to the individual drug. Previously a list was provided identifying short, intermediate acting, and long acting medications. Some of the drugs have a very short duration (i.e. halcion) while others have a long half-life (i.e. valium) and are stored in the body fat, bones, and muscles. They will eliminate themselves in the time needed. Elimination of a drug from your body system can only be estimated. A formula sometimes used is to take the half-life of the drug and multiply it by a factor of four. Look up the medication you are taking, find the half-life and multiply it by the aforementioned factor. At best you will have obtained only an estimated time for elimination.

Half-Life for Xanax and Valium

Assume the prescribed dose for Xanax is 1 mg., Q.I.D., (four times a day). The half-life is 15–16 hours or the better part of a day. Valium has a half life of approximately 3 days. In the following chart, the figure below the line represents the carryover effect while the top figure is the total amount the doctor prescribed. With Valium we will work with the following prescription: 5 mg., Q.I.D. However to make the equation more understandable a fictional half-life of one day will be substituted.

137

	Xanax (1 mg., Q.I.D.)		**Valium** (5mg., Q.I.D., fictional half-life of one day)
Day 1	4mg. (daily dose)	Day 1	20mg. (daily dose)
Day 2	4mg. (daily) 2mg. (1/2 life)	Day 2	20mg. (daily) 10mg. (1/2 life)*
Day 3	4mg. (daily) 3mg. (1/2 life)	Day 3	20mg. (daily) 15mg. (1/2 life)*
Day 4	4mg. (daily 3.5mg. (1/2 life)	Day 4	20mg. (daily) 17.5mg. (1/2 life)*
Day 5	4mg. (daily) 3.75mg. (1/2 life)	Day 5	20mg. (daily) 18.75mg. (1/2 life)*
Day 6	4mg. (daily) 3.9mg. (1/2 life)	Day 6	20mg. (daily) 19.30mg. (1/2 life)*
Day 7	4mg. (daily) 4mg. (1/2 life)	Day 7	20mg. (daily) 20mg. (1/2 life)*
Day 8	4mg. (daily) 4mg. (1/2 life)	Day 8	20mg. (daily) 20mg. (1/2 life)*

*DESMETHYLDIAZEPAM

As you can see the residual dose accumulates and reaches an approximation of the prescribed daily dose within a week. It would not alter the effective dose if you forgot to take a pill every now and then. In the case of Valium, the drug produces a psychoactive metabolite Desmethyldiazepam. The various pills are manufactured for the purpose of lasting a brief or longer time.

Symptom Generation or Symptom Re-emergence

The next chart represents a comparison of the relative intensity and time course of Valium withdrawal symptoms. Other long acting Benzodiazepines will conform to this profile:

1. The symptom generation syndrome has been described in this chapter as a withdrawal reaction. It is a sedative hypnotic type withdrawal set of symptoms.

2. The symptom re-emergence syndrome is the resurfacing of the feelings associated with the problems that led to the taking of the medication in the first place. This re-emergence syndrome may not occur if the patient has resolved conflicts which led to the initial use and dependence of these drugs.

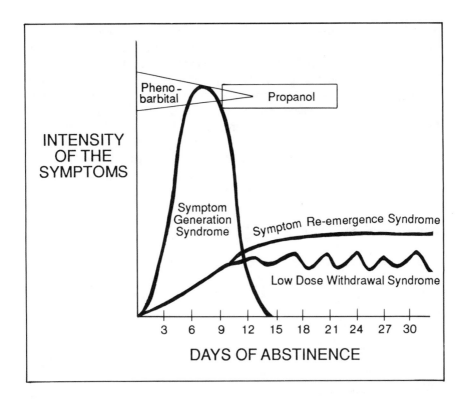

INTENSITY OF THE SYMPTOMS

Pheno-barbital

Propanol

Symptom Generation Syndrome

Symptom Re-emergence Syndrome

Low Dose Withdrawal Syndrome

3 6 9 12 15 18 21 24 27 30

DAYS OF ABSTINENCE

3. The low-dose withdrawal syndrome can be a prolonged period with episodic clusters of increasing and decreasing symptoms following the acute phase. The brain is trying to heal itself. The patient must understand that there will be good days and bad ones. Anxiety and insomnia are common. However if psychiatric problems are severe, re-medication may be necessary. The patient may be illustrating signs of an underlying endogenous psychiatric disorder. Depression may be a symptom of a dual diagnosis, a seperate disorder from symptoms and disorders associated with the withdrawal reaction.

4. Benzodiazepines have specific receptor-sites in the brain which will undergo a withdrawal syndrome once the drug is discontinued. This reaction is usually mild and masked by the more attention getting problems.

Dual Diagnosis

There is no greater incidence of psychiatric illness in the alcoholic than the public at large. The alcoholic must strive for total abstinence and not transfer addictions to another drug. When using unprescribed drugs a variety of

139

psychiatric and behavioral disorders will manifest themselves. Most behavioral symptoms clear up in recovery as there is no organic brain dysfunction. However some people have what is known as a dual diagnosis.

A successful dual diagnosis approach is one that views the patient as suffering from chemical dependency and a co-existing psychiatric problem.

Among the adult population, the psychiatric diagnoses most commonly found in the dual diagnosis patient are: schizophrenia, manic depressive illness, major depression, post traumatic stress syndrome, organic brain syndrome and borderline personality. Among the adolescent population, the dual disordered child suffers from depression, conduct disorders, schizophrenia, organic brain syndrome and hyperactivity.

Withdrawal Symptoms

To prevent undesirable or hazardous symptoms it may be necessary to gradually stop taking any of the benzodiazepine medications. Talk it over with your physician. Enter into a gradual reduction to mimimize the withdrawal complications.

The symptoms of withdrawal will vary from one person to another. Most people addicted to the benzodiazepines would be expected to experience some combination of the following symptoms when the drug is discontinued abruptly or during a gradual reduction. The latter program will be easier to go through.

———————————— QUOTATION ————————————

"If we were to stop abruptly the availability of this drug (Valium), our country would be in an epidemic of anxious, neurotic, psychotic, trembling, paranoid citizens in acute withdrawal"

Testimony given September 10, 1979, before the Senate Subcommittee on Health and Research. Senator Edward M. Kennedy, Chairman on Diazepine a Hazard To Our Health.

The pill addict of this type can expect to undergo an increase in anxiety. That's usually why most people began taking a tranquilizer in the first place. Initially the panic and anxiety will be greater than the original symptoms. Part of this fear is generated by knowing that you are going through detoxification. The desire to take the medication is high, because it's so effective. It seems abnormal to suffer through all this when you know how to eliminate these feelings.

Don't plan on getting a lot done because you probably will have disorganized thinking, poor comprehension, loss of concentration, confusion, and poor judgment which obviously means intellectual impairment with memory deficit. All these symptoms are aggravated since this unfortunate addict is restless and probably won't sleep very well. Sweaty feet slip and slide on the floor. Just to let you know you're not going insane, you might experience vertigo as well as bad dreams, gastro-intestinal problems, agitation, violence, peculiar mood, depression and gran mal seizures. During withdrawal, your head may feel as though it is being gently squeezed.

Withdrawal symptoms occur: 1) after large doses of drugs for a few days; 2) after moderate doses over a few months, and 3) after minimal doses for a few years. In the last instance, physical dependence proves that the drug and its metabolites are accumulated and stored in the body for long periods of time.

It is only during the last few years that attention has been focused on the dependency produced in the low-dose (therapeutic) range. In one study of 32 people, almost half of those who had taken an average of 10 mg. of Valium per day for four months to several years developed withdrawal symptoms. In another study of ten people using an average dose of 17 mg. of Valium for over one year, all developed withdrawal symptoms.

Early signs of dependence may be missed or misdiagnosed due to the fact that anxiety is usually the dominant withdrawal symptom. Discrimination between the recurrence of pre-treatment anxiety and withdrawal symptoms can be problematic for the physician as well as the patient.

Exercise extreme patience, discomforting symptoms will diminish. Be good to yourself, don't purposely enter into unnecessary stressful situations. Always have a back up plan. Use it if you start to be overwhelmed. Lastly, don't quit five minutes before the miracle.

Panic Attacks

Panic attacks can cause a great deal of distress during withdrawal. The sufferer is suddenly overwhelmed by fear for no apparent reason, and often feels that death is not far away. Some feel unable to move or speak, others shout for help. Although the attacks usually last only a few minutes it can seem much longer to the sufferer.

A person who is nervous, has the "butterflies", is sweating, and experiences a rise in heart rate, may be having a normal response to stress. A panic attack is an exaggeration of this normal reaction. Agoraphobia, a morbid fear of open spaces, is one of the more common symptoms of panic disorders. If you are over-enthusiastic the first time you go out jogging, your muscles may complain the next day, by being stiff and sore. Panic attacks, agoraphobia, irritability, and many other symptoms are a similiar cry for help from your nervous system. It is saying "Do not use me, I have had enough." Limited research indicates that cocaine and methamphetamine addicts will experience a disproportionate number of panic reactions. This will

141

also occur during the rehabilitation period, though at reduced frequency. These drugs obviously exhaust the nervous system.

Every symptom of a wildly beating heart, rapid breathing, sweating and shaking is part of a "flight or fright" response. We would be lost without it. We do not want to stop it, but to get it back to normal. The anxious person tends to overbreathe while the depressed person often inhales shallowly and exhales deeply.

The treatment for hyperventilation is to temporarily rebreathe exhaled air. Breathing into a paper bag is a useful method to increase carbon dioxide levels in the blood.

Lithium Treatment for Psychiatric Disorders

Two psychiatrists of the University of Oregon Health Science Center in Portland report that lithium, which is one of the simplest of all elements, exerts a profound effect on human behavior.

The third element in the periodic table was first identified in 1817 although not isolated until until 1855. It is the lightest of all solids and is chemically related to sodium and potassium. It was used in Australia in the treatment of mania, a type of mental illness in which overtalkativeness, grandiose ideas, restlessness, excessive irritability with swings in mood are characteristic. It was not until about 1960, however, that Danish researchers convinced psychiatrists of its great value in the treatment of manic-depressions. It took until 1969 for lithium to be approved for use in the United States.

Lithium is most valuable in the treatment of mental illness in which mood cycles are prominent, both the highs of mania and the lows of depression. Many studies have now shown that lithium can bring attacks of mania to an end and can prevent most future episodes. A 30-year old male talked about his manic periods. A typical episode would begin with restlessness in the form of pacing about followed by continuous driving between San Francisco and Big Sur, California. The one way mileage is about 150 miles and he would average three or four round trips. Inevitably, he would end up in the psychiatric hospital until his medications could be adjusted to an effective dose.

Depressive episodes can also be prevented. Lithium is used to treat depression alone, without evidence of mania. In this type of illness, the victim usually feels hopeless and pessimistic, may feel guilty about some mistake which is real or imaginary and may develop delusions about some bodily illness. Social contacts are apt to be shunned and sadness may be the only expressed emotion.

A manic-depressive often fluctuates between episodes of mania and states of depression. These moods have genetic and biochemical foundations. These are the kinds of mood for which lithium has the greatest value. On the other hand it would have no place in the treatment of depressions over circumstances due to divorce, death in the family and similiar events. Only the depressions that come from within because of biochemical changes are helped by lithium.

Some alcoholic-cocaine addicts have responded favorably to lithium. Both of the drugs disrupt the normal neuro-chemistry of the brain, especially after prolonged usage. The concurrent use of alcohol and cocaine produces a manic-depressive effect. Lithium can be expected to have a better result if the patient is drug free. In addition, lithium is far superior to tranquilizers in the treatment of mania. The patient is not under the influence of a sedative. The patient is calmer and is in a truly stabilized mood rather than a suppressed condition. The element appears to have a truly normalizing effect, at least for a time.

Things People Say When They Are Getting Better

1. I woke up thinking pleasurably about having a cup of coffee instead of worrying how I would get through the day.
2. I could feel the effects that my depression was having on those close to me.
3. I saw my son fall in love and become engaged. I was capable of being happy in his joy.
4. I actually started a conversation.
5. I was dreading changing the electronic fuel injection system in my old car, so I gave it away. I was proud of my decision.
6. I was half way through my commute to work when I realized that I was not resenting every minute of it.
7. I forced myself to clean off my desk and complete all deliquent paperwork, then was astonished to find that two hours had passed.

Summary

Benzodiazepine is the technical term for a tranquilizer. Benzodiazepines relieve tensions and anxieties and produce muscle relaxation, but when used excessively may produce habituation and addiction. Personalities and emotions of certain individuals may predispose them to the use of these drugs and addiction.

Thalidomide, a benzodiazepine, was thought to be safe. When it was used during pregnancy it resulted in worldwide tragedy. Babies were born with all manner of serious deformities. Some were dead at birth or shortly thereafter.

Some drugs may interact with others in the body to produce unexpected results and toxic reactions. There are currently about 800 benzodiazepines on the world market. The longer an active drug is in the body the more extended its effects, whether they are "good or bad."

There is a general medical consensus that after long use of benzodiazepines their use should be tapered off slowly rather than being suddenly terminated in order to prevent serious withdrawal complications.

The symptom re-emergence syndrome consists of the same feelings that were present in the beginning when treatment was first started. These conflicts may have been resolved through professional treatment while taking this type of medication, and therefore may not resurface.

Self-Test On Benzodiazepines

1. A technical name for tranquilizers is: (A) benzodiazepines; (B) chlortetracyclines; (C) heptaldehydes; (D) none of the foregoing.

2. Tranquilizers may produce: (A) too much of a desired result; (B) an allergic reaction; (C) reactivation of a prior illness; (D) reactions with other drugs in the body; (E) any or all of the foregoing responses.

3. The shorter the half-life of a benzodiazepine: (A) the longer it lasts in the body; (B) the quicker its effects are apt to disappear; (C) the more severe any damaging effect will be; (D) has little to do with the beneficial result; (E) the more addictive it will be.

4. An iatrogenic illness is one caused by: (A) alcohol; (B) other drugs; (C) a preceding sickness; (D) poor nutrition; (E) the doctor.

5. A person addicted to valium is most apt to recognize the problem when: (A) the dosage is increased; (B) the drug is discontinued; (C) it is combined with another sedative-hypnotic; (D) it is taken with a drink of alcohol; (E) taken with another drug.

6. When thalidomide was used during pregnancy by women around the world: (A) the drug proved to be safe; (B) it was approved by the Food and Drug Administration in the United States; (C) it caused thousands of babies to be born with serious deformities; (D) the drug was finally approved and used in the United States; (E) none of the foregoing.

7. Agoraphobia, a morbid fear of open spaces, is one of the more common symptoms of: (A) effort syndrome; (B) panic attacks; (C) mange; (D) manic-depressive illness; (E) bulimarexia.

8. Identify the medication that is far superior to tranquilizers in the treatment of mania: (A) Xanax; (B) Stelazine; (C) dopamine; (D) Lithium; (E) Naltrexone.

Answers: 1(A); 2(E); 3(B); 4(E); 5(B); 6(C); 7(B); 8(D).

144

Notes

1. From the Drug Newsletter No. 31, April 1985. Regional Drug Information Service, Newcastle upon Tyne.

Bibliography

1. Silverman, Harold M. *The Pill Book, Guide to Safe Pill Use.* 470 pp. Bantam Books, New York, New York, 1989.
2. Smith, Dorothy L., Pharm. D., *Understanding Prescription Drugs.* 504 pp., Pocket Books, New York, New York, 1987.
3. Trickett, Shirley. *Coming Off Tranquilizers.* 110 pp. Thorsons Publishing Group, New York, New York, 1986.
4. Handlly, Robert. *Anxiety and Panic Attacks.* 257 pp. Fawcet Crest, New York, New York, 1985.
5. Bargman, Eve M.D., Sidney Wolf M.D., Joan Levin and The Public Citizen Health Research Group. *Stopping Valium.* 178 pp. Warner Books, Washington D.C., 1983.
6. Marks, John. *The Benzodiazepines,* 111 pp. MTP Press Limited, St. Leonards House, Lancaster, England, 1978.

CHAPTER NINE

Narcotics, Designer Drugs and the Impaired Health Professional, Understanding AIDS

Introduction

Addiction to the opiates is an ancient world problem. Heroin appears to be the most addictive of the drugs derived from opium. The use of this synthetic by the medical profession has been outlawed for some years. In recent times, however, the illicit use of heroin has increased substantially. It is difficult to tell the magnitude of heroin addiction in the United States but there is evidence that the cocaine epidemic has fueled the use of heroin.

It is likely that the use of heroin stems primarily from the disturbed personality of the addict, although cultural, sociological, inherent occupational and other factors may be contributing factors. The medical and nursing professions contain high-risk job-related hazards because of the closeness to the use of narcotics for the relief of pain and suffering. There are some differences in categories of addiction but consistent patterns of personality differences can be found in all.

The detection and diagnosis of narcotic addiction is often not a simple matter. The heroin addict who receives the drug is apt to be at peace with the world until the need for more leads to antisocial behaviors. There is a ceaseless quest for the next supply of drugs.

There are numerous undesirable effects from the use of heroin, some of which are indirect and related to other behaviors. The multiple use of other drugs, infections caused by contaminated needles, the addiction of babies before birth and fatal overdosages are only a part of the hazard with this drug.

The heroin user tends to withdraw from problems and inadequacies and to escape tensions, pain and frustration by use of a drug, whereas the amphetamine user attempts to solve fundamentally similiar problems through the use of a drug that produces feelings of energy, competency and superiority. There is a fundamental sense of low self-esteem in both classes of drug addicts. The amphetamine user inflates self-respect, whereas the heroin user seeks chemical escape through the use of an opiate.

Most people will not use heroin, but at some time in their lives will take narcotics under the guidance of a doctor. The reason drugs work is because they stimulate the brain's own endogenous (produced within the organism) receptor sites.

The Impaired Health Professional

Characteristics of The Impaired Nurse

The following observations were gathered from 90 registered nurses forced into treatment by their employers for addiction to narcotics and other controlled substances. Typically, the facility notifies the State Board of Registered Nurses which will report the complaint to the Drug Diversion Program. The suspected nurse will not be informed of the person or persons who filed the report. There are four avenues that can be taken. First, nothing may happen. The charges were unfounded. Second, the license can be suspended. Third, the nurse can be put on probation. The employee will have to follow the conditions set forth during the probationary period. The impaired nurse will have to submit to treatment and periodic urine testing or suffer loss of license and membership in the profession. Fourth, the license may be revoked.

The rate of alcoholism in nurses is roughly one in ten, which is close to what should be expected. The incidence of narcotic addiction is two to three percent which is similiar to that found among physicians.

There is no stereotypical nurse or doctor-addict. Some health professionals are hooked on stimulants like cocaine, while others use depressants like alcohol or opiates like demerol and fentanyl. Some must dose themselves around the clock, while others can wait until after work. Some mix drugs. Perhaps cocaine or methamphetamine by day, and then an opiate or alcohol or Xanax at night to come down. There is no way to predict when an addiction will impair performance, particularly in its early stages. The addicted health professional doesn't just show up loaded one day at work. It's a progressive disease. After a certain point, the addict will have to use the drug to feel normal. The cure is exactly what's killing you.

Another part of the explanation for a surprisingly proficient performance lies in the *"paradox of opiates"*. Most people tend to view intoxication by looking at alcohol, but unlike that drug, narcotics can leave the addict apparently clear-headed and steady. They generally cause little organic damage or none that can be recognized. Taking narcotics would be as physiologically harmless as eating corn flakes if it weren't for rising tolerance and the steady increase in the amount needed to get high. This is not to say that addicted health professionals are functioning at their best. If the impaired health professionals aren't overcome by drugs themselves, their efforts to get the ever-increasing amount of drugs they need will implicate the addiction.

The nursing group was found to be distinctly different from the average addict. First, the nurses became addicted as adults, not as adolescents, and began using drugs to relieve pain or for escape from stresses rather than for "kicks." Most addicted nurses don't think anything of pilfering oral narcotics when relief is needed. Their drug use was a solitary experience rather than in the company of others. Nurses did not resort to prostitution, shoplifting, or other measures to obtain their drugs but instead used theft in the working situation, prescriptions by physicians, or forged prescriptions to obtain their drugs.

The impaired nurse will become overinvolved with the drug cabinet. Addicted nurses are interested in pharmaceutical samples. Nurses interested in drugs like to work for the registry as they can be assigned to a variety of health care facilities, always looking, yet remaining somewhat anonymous. Working an unsupervised shift is preferable. A performance profile will include some of the following behaviors, such as coming to work early and staying late. If a nurse were to draw up 20 mg. of morphine sulfate, she would have to replace the missing volume with sterile water. Patients may begin to complain that their pain medication isn't working. Nurses are required to complete written records of their patients prior to the next shift. The impaired nurse tends to keep sloppy charts. Long lunches are not unusual. Phoning in prescriptions is commonplace, the Drug Enforcement (DEA) number of the physician will be known. If the pharmacist calls back to the office, the nurse can verify the authenticity of the order. A nurse will be clever, not ordering drugs that will attract attention. Wholesale drug companies can be another source, especially in the medical office. Behavior becomes unpredictable.

Most of the nurse-addicts came from stable and intact homes and most of them had close relationships with their families. There has been no background of childhood or adolescent problems severe enough to bring them to the attention of the law. Finally, they are more intelligent and better educated than the average addict.

The major conclusion about the impaired nurses seems to be that they resort to drugs because of pressures and problems that cannot be handled. After rehabilitation the impaired nurses feel more comfortable if they work in situations where narcotics are not needed by the patient.

Impaired Physicians

In medicine, nursing, dentistry, pharmacy and certain paramedical sciences where access to drugs may exist, there is always the potential that a person may begin to use them. Addiction to drugs is considered an occupational hazard of the field of medicine.

According to George Vaillant in an article entitled, "Physicians' Use of Mood-Altering Drugs", published in the New England Journal of Medicine, the approximate incidence of alcoholism in physicians is estimated at about five percent, and narcotic addiction runs from two to three percent. The abuse of alcohol and mood-altering drugs may be the most common sign of psychiatric illness in physicians. Among doctors admitted for psychiatric reasons to the Mayo Clinic it was found that 50 percent showed dependence on alcohol or drugs, and that 23 percent were dependent on both. There is other evidence that physicians in general abuse drugs more than the population at large. Over a period of 25 years about 1/2 to 1 percent of licensed physicians in the state of New York were reported as narcotic addicts. Many physicians were able to conceal their problem through resignation and relocation. In contrast, only about 1 in 1,000 American males in the age group 20 to 50 years becomes addicted to narcotics and most of these addicts come from the streets.

"Physicians have a rate of addiction to prescription narcotics that's four to six times higher than the general population's," says David Smith, M.D. The toll among anesthesiologists is so high that addiction is now considered an occupational hazard. Only 20,000, or four percent, of doctors are anesthesiologists, yet they represent 13 percent of doctors treated for addiction. There are two special factors at work in the case of anesthesiologists. They encounter life-and-death tensions of surgery but, unlike surgeons, they play only an intermittent, though crucial, role. It's like being a sailor, ninety–five percent tedium and five percent terror. These physicians have easy access to highly addictive drugs that usually aren't available to other doctors. Anaesthetics such as fentanyl can be requisitioned at the discretion of physicians from the hospital pharmacy for their patients.

There are several reasons why a disproportionately high percentage of physicians get into trouble with drugs. The most obvious is that pharmaceuticals are more readily available to them. They also work under a peculiar kind of stress. They are expected to make no mistakes in treating their patients. It is their responsibility to cure serious illness and prevent death, and to suppress their emotions in doing so. When stress becomes unbearable, they are surrounded by instant ways to alleviate it. Initially, any dose of morphine will put you in a state of euphoria. But soon the "euphoric window" begins to shrink, and *the all-consuming goal becomes avoiding the agonies of withdrawal.* Feeding a habit without arousing suspicion becomes a monumental task, aggravated by exhaustion, secrecy, guilt and fear that tomorrow's fixes won't be so easy to come by. The addict will lose self-esteem, family, the will to live and eventually the competence to practice medicine.

A sharp distinction needs to be drawn between the average doctor's considerable technical knowledge of drugs and their effects, and the near-ignorance of the disease of addiction. Doctors often think they're too intelligent and knowledgeable to get addicted. Medical schools must assume a more important role in orienting their students that they represent a high risk population for drug abuse.

The Impaired Physicians Program of the Medical Association of Georgia, at the Ridgeview Institute in Smyrna, Georgia, is the world's largest treatment center for addicted doctors, nurses, dentists and pharmacists.

Relapse and the Impaired Health Professional

Relapse is of major concern to all persons recovering from chemical dependency. Currently research in relapse prevention is zeroing in on what happens before the person resumes chemical use. Numerous studies have linked stress with relapse. When an event, internal or external, happens and causes change or stress, symptoms occur. If not managed, the symptoms become so severe that chemical use comes to look like a positive option.

As the relapse process worsens, behavioral cues become visible to others. A cue means nothing to a person who doesn't have a drug history. To a recovering addict, a cue may trigger chemical-using thoughts. The professional in recovery begins to doubt the ability to stay sober. Impaired health professionals most certainly will have their licences revoked if they do not respond to treatment by achieving a chemically free life.

The person may then be tempted to seek comfort in impulsive acts, such as an apparent geographical cure. Denial prevents the recovering health professional from dealing with the stress. Internal stress continues to build and makes life more uncomfortable. Friends are driven away by the addict's defensiveness, isolation and depression. The relaspe process is well under way.

Physical demands of the job revolve around responsibility and pressure. Often the physician or nurse will have to hold still for long periods of time, either one-to-one or on a ward full of persons who are actively in crisis, emotionally reactive, and often prone to acute infections. The health care professional may work long hours and attribute this to the urgency of the work. Exhaustion is a symptom of relapse. Don't allow yourself to become overly tired or in poor health. Good health and enough rest are important. Many health professionals are prone to work addictions, when attempting to make up for lost time given to active addiction.

The cognitive demands on nurses are great. Trends towards greater accountability and decreasing resources put the nurse in a position of doing more with less. A confused sense of mission causes distress as paperwork demands multiply with patient census. Nurses must be adept at balancing the demands of their agency with the needs of their patients. The tendency to nurture will always be there, privately hoping for lasting gratitude, but also ready to catapult the nurse into compulsive caretaking. Two problems, over-involvement with patients and projection of problems, are self-defeating. Internal stress hastens the relapse process. High expectations can contribute to personal problems. The higher your expectations, the more likely the disappointment. Results usually fall between the highs and lows, realistic expectations will reduce the frequency of personal disappointment.

Relapse is not inevitable, and the process is reversible. Health professionals do need to know their own symptoms and practice early recognition of relapse warning signs. It is important to learn how to manage the stress that produces these symptoms.

Do not set goals you cannot reach with normal efforts. It's always great when good things happen. You will get what you are entitled to as long as you do your best, but maybe not as soon as you think you should.

Patient Susceptibility

The idea of individual susceptibility to addiction helps explain why hospital patients treated with opiates rarely become addicts. Then, the setting for drug use is hardly recreational. They are given to treat physical pain, they are not self-administered, and they are usually given for short periods only. Even when a patient develops a physiological addiction after taking large amounts of narcotics during an extended illness or recovery from injury, the withdrawal is usually brief and easily managed. Often the hospital patient doesn't even know what is happening.

QUESTION

What are Propoxyphene and Meperidine?

Propoxyphene is the generic name for Darvon, a synthetic analgesic. Meperidine, a narcotic analgesic, is also known as Demerol. Both are highly abused prescription medications.[1]

A most interesting television program on Parkinson's disease was featured in 1987 in a PBS Nova special entitled "The Case of the Frozen Addict." The show documented the disastrous instances in which designer drugs were not correctly manufactured. One case involved a botched batch of a compound called MPPP, an analog of the pain killer meperidine (Demerol). The drug turned out to contain MPTP, a deadly neurotoxin that has created a syndrome like Parkinson's disease in more than 400 drug abusers, most of them in California. The victims were board stiff and totally dependent on medical care. Eventual treatment involved L-Dopa, a drug which produced remarkable improvement in the immobolized addicts. Ironically, the tragedy has led to important medical insights into the chemical causes of Parkinsonism.

Designer Opiates

Fentanyl is manufactured by a pharmaceutical firm in Belgium, an affiliate of Johnson and Johnson. It was introduced into the United States in 1972 under the brand name Sublimaze. Its attraction for surgery lies in its ability to produce potent, short-lived, and reversible anaesthesia. It is used by the same opiate receptors in the brain that heroin and morphine use, which means an addict can maintain a habit on any of these opiate drugs. It was intially thought that a dose strong enough to give a high without rendering the user unconscious wouldn't last long enough to be practical for an addict who wants to stay intoxicated all day.

That limitation was overcome in 1979, when a "street chemist" changed fentanyl's molecular structure and increased its potency and staying power. Small amounts are needed to produce a high. Overdose is common and so is respiratory arrest. Some heroin addicts look for fentanyl because some people have died from it, so it must be good. The first compound the chemist released was alpha-methyl fentanyl, known as China White. A later modification, 3-methyl fentanyl lasts as long as a shot of heroin. Fentanyl's strength is hard to exaggerate. It's one hundred times as strong as morphine, and 20 to 40 times as strong as heroin. Its medicinal analogs, sufentanyl and lofentanyl, are respectively, 2,000 and 6,000 times as strong as morphine. While this sort of potency makes fentanyl an effective anaesthetic, its ultra-fast rush results in stronger addiction than any street narcotic. It can take years to become addicted to alcohol, months for cocaine, and one shot for fentanyl. Illegal fentanyl is even available in different grades for shooters and snorters.

The designer chemists have extensive scientific knowledge of fentanyl. Anticipating the legal-analog game, the chemists have made as many as two dozen designer versions. The skilled designer chemists manipulate the drug's structure slightly to avoid by a molecule or two the regulations that govern it without losing any of its potency. According to federal drug laws, a compound is legal until declared otherwise. When they first hit the streets, most designer drugs were as legal as herbal tea. New, and legal, analogs are being released once the Federal Drug Administration has identified and classified other variations as being illegal.

153

"[Designer drugs are] drug version of Chernobyl and the kind of problem, unimaginable twenty years ago. A direct response to the increasingly high-tech, scientific orientation of our society."
Gene Haislip

Some General Conclusions

Opiates (Narcotics)

Chronic use is usually not harmful to the body*
Can cause death by respiratory depression
Kills pain better than most other drugs
Are the best anti-diarrheal medications
Are the best anti-tussive medications (cough suppressants)
Produce physical dependence
Cause tolerance and cross tolerance

Central Nervous System (CNS) Depressants

Chronic use can be harmful to the body
Can cause death by respiratory depression
Has properties of tolerance and cross tolerance
Can produce reverse tolerance
Are physically addicting

Physical Dependence: A syndrome of predictable physical symptoms which ensue when someone stops using a drug suddenly (A Property of the Drug). Withdrawal symptoms are opposite to the primary effect of the drug. A CNS depressant will cause arousal and agitation. A narcotic withdrawal will include diarrhea, as the drug will cause constipation.

Psychological Dependence: A psychological craving to use a drug (A Property of the Person).

Tolerance and Withdrawal

Addiction to these drugs will bring tolerance, medical complications, withdrawal, and behavioral oddity. *Tolerance* is the need to increase the dose in order to achieve the desired effect. *Withdrawal* has various characteristic signs and symptoms. When a drug is suddenly removed, the cells

---

* Most narcotics-related diseases and deaths are caused by overdosage, secondary problems like malnutrition, or infections from dirty drugs or needles. Excessive use of aspirin or Acetaminophen with codeine may cause kidney, liver and internal bleeding. Large amounts of aspirin can damage hearing.

cannot function normally until the body becomes able to produce or use its own biochemicals properly. Until then, there is the withdrawal period with symptoms different in onset and duration for each drug. Narcotic addicts will find alternative drugs when their supply runs out. The barbiturates are often used as a substitute. Amobarbital, secobarbital (reds) and tuinal (reds and blues) can all be injected. Tuinal is most sought after by the experienced street addict.

Many heroin addicts detox two or three times a year just to prove they can do it and to reduce their tolerance. The six most common withdrawal symptoms from narcotics are diarrhea, stomach cramps, runny nose, muscle aches, insomnia and tachycardia.

Cross Tolerance

Cross-tolerance tends to develop among users of drugs in the same class. Drugs have been grouped together in Chapter 1. Once you have acquired tolerance to a psychoactive drug, you will have acquired equivalent tolerance to other related drugs. For example, you have a kidney stone that won't pass through excretion. Your doctor has been prescribing increasing doses of codeine and then switches you to Darvon. You will need just as much of it and receive as little effect, if the two drugs have a cross tolerance.

There are two kinds of dependency: physical and psychological. In physical dependency the substance becomes biochemically necessary for body cells to function normally. The sedative-hypnotics and narcotics produce physical dependency. The stimulants are believed to cause a primarily psychological dependence.

Reverse Tolerance

Chronic use can be harmful to the body. Alcohol is toxic to every cell of the body and it is a powerful immunosuppressive drug. Research studies show that alcohol interferes with the capacity of the brain to pay attention to simultaneous inputs of information and the thinking that would normally be expected. Degeneration of the brain occurs from heavy consumption of alcohol. The use of drug combinations will accelerate physical degenerative effects. Thinking is impaired, drunk or sober.

A primary drug is the drug of preference. It is by no means the only drug that will be taken. Alcohol is constantly included in drug combinations. It may not be the preferred psychoactive agent, but ethanol runs a close second. Normally the liver metabolizes fats. However, when alcohol is introduced into the body, the preferred fuel becomes alcohol. Fats begin to accumulate in the liver. Reverse tolerance indicates the alcoholic needs a longer time than normal for the drug to be metabolized into simpler compounds, a sign of a partially non-functioning liver.

Narcotics

All narcotics are opiates. Some are natural, others are synthetic. Morphine is the part of opium that gives the latter its pain-killing qualities. Opium, codeine, morphine, heroin and a number of other drugs of a like nature are classified as narcotic analgesics (pain killers). Such drugs are the alkaloids of morphine. An alkaloid is one of a large group of organic, basic substances found in plants. They are usually bitter in taste and physiologically active. Examples of these substances are atropine, caffeine, morphine, nicotine, cocaine, quinine and many others. The term is also applied to synthetic substances which have structures similar to plant alkaloids, such as procaine.

Morphine is the chief narcotic principle of opium. The pod contains approximately 10 percent morphine, 2.5 percent codeine and 87.5 percent inert ingredients. Diacetyl morphine is heroin. Methyl morphine is codeine. Opiates are more effective when injected into the body. Heroin can be injected, smoked or snorted. Other narcotics such as codeine, demerol and darvon can be taken orally. About 62 percent of the codeine gets into the blood stream when taken orally. If the same dose is injected, blood levels of the drug will be higher.

The effect of morphine and related drugs is to decrease feelings of fatigue, hunger, discomfort, pain and other disagreeable sensations. There is a depression of attention and sometimes a mental fog with somewhat larger doses. In overdosage, there is constriction of the pupils to pin-point size, dryness of the mouth, thirst, constipation because of effects on the gastric and intestinal muscles, reduction of body temperature and decreased urine output. In the hospital the standard for intra-muscular injection of morphine is about 10 mg., but the dose is prescribed for the individual patient. The dosage will vary and should not produce all of the foregoing symptoms.

Heroin is transformed into morphine in the body. It is a longer acting drug. Morphine is converted into numerous inert drugs. It is not as potent as the parent drug, heroin. What kills heroin addicts is pulmonary edema and respiratory depression, drug combinations (synergism), cutting substances and many infections because of contamination. Because heroin and related drugs are apt to be given by injection into veins, health complications are frequent due to the lack of proper sterilization of injection needles and exposure to communicable diseases. Some of these complications are skin abscesses, inflammation of blood vessels (track marks), blood clots, lung damage from circulating clots, pneumonia, lung abscesses, infection of the liver (hepatitis) and inflammation and bacterial infection of the tissues of the heart.

Symptoms of overdosage include a gradual development of unconsciousness and coma, symmetrical pin-point pupils (although the pupils may dilate as death approaches), relaxation of muscles (for example, the jaw may drop) and slow irregular and depressed respiration that may lead to cardiac arrest. Death is almost always due to depression of respiration and the maximum interference with breathing can be expected to occur within about seven minutes after an injection of morphine into the veins. Injections into the muscles or under the skin may cause maximum depression of respiration within 30 to 90 minutes later. Side effects can be produced including nausea, vomiting and impairment of thinking.

Most heroin is of poor quality. Probably, there is already an epidemic of heroin and cocaine use in this decade. Cocaine has been accepted into the middle class. Use of the drug has expanded beyond the ghetto. Fentanyl is a synthetic form of heroin which is extremely potent and is responsible for numerous accidental overdose deaths. Narcotics bought on "the street" are often adulterated with quinine, lactose, sucrose, procaine, magnesium silicate, mannitol or other substances.

Viet Nam Vets and Heroin

The Vietnam experience makes clear the kind of pressures that may drive a person otherwise not addiction-prone to become an addict. For many soldiers in combat areas, fear and discomfort were everpresent. Not only were these men in danger of losing their lives, but they were deprived of the security and reassurance people expect from their environments. Many Viet Nam Veterans got hooked on extremely potent grades of heroin and other drugs, including alcohol during the war. Not all the soldiers who were addicted to heroin in Vietnam were in combat situations and therefore not in active danger. However, they were all out of control of their lives —that is, their basic life choices were not in their own hands. A feeling of powerlessness, of being unable to influence one's situation in a positive way, is as great a factor in addiction as fear.

Of crucial importance for the soldier addict was the absence of close relationships and the loss of meaningful work. Without their families, lovers, wives, and friends to provide intimacy, they looked to narcotics for substitute gratification. At the same time, the narcotic experience concealed the futility of their individual actions as well as that of the war effort.

When it was time to return to the United States, the Army tried to make sure the soldier didn't come home addicted. To the surprise of some drug abuse experts, most of the men who were detoxed were able to stay drug free once they got home. While they had abused a very addictive drug, they lacked the genetic and psychological components of true addiction. Now, with neuroscientists and geneticists bringing their expertise to the study of addiction, many researchers have come to think of it as a disease in which a biological irregularity encoded in the genes is fueled by misuse of the drug. Once the stress of war was over only about 10 percent continued addictive use after returning home. The challenge to society still remains.

Methadone Treatment

In the past, treatment of heroin addiction has been characterized by almost constant failure. The emergence of the methadone treatment plan does not result in the cure of a narcotic addict. Methadone itself is a powerful narcotic and can be used as a substitute for heroin. Methadone is legal, longer acting, is produced in a measured dose, and is pure. Tablet and liquid forms are most commonly available.

The treatment objective is two fold. First, supply the addict with methadone and the user can abandon a life of crime for a job or school and family revival. Second, achieve withdrawal of the addict from heroin by the use of methadone. The addict can be taken off a lengthy heroin addiction in a matter of days. Now the person has a short term methadone addiction. Heroin is absent from the body, another drug has been substituted. Clonidine, another drug, can be used to block opiate withdrawal. The complications of multiple drug withdrawal are lessened. Theoretically, all this specific drug transference will lead to a chemically free life. In the final analysis, the naked face must look into the mirror of life. It's an inside job.

_____ QUOTATION _____

"Granted that I must die, how shall I live?

Michael Novak

Diminishing doses and individual or group therapy is the goal. If the initial dose of methadone is 70mg., and the patient is doing well, the physician may decide to reduce the level of medication to 60 mg. One of the problems is that methadone is harder to get off of than heroin. Addicts can testify to this fact. Methadone doesn't alter addictive lifestyle patterns, however it does provide time to stop searching for the primary drug. Interests in recovery can be implanted. Personality reorientation is a lifetime goal. The addict needs to start looking for the personal and social factors that are related to the escape behaviors of drug usage.

Methadone Overdosage

Victims of methadone overdosage are apt to show diminished consciousness, a slow heart rate and a reduction in breathing. In some of the victims there is likely to be a slight decrease in the size of the pupils. Of the patients in one study who were treated by an injection of Narcan (a narcotic antagonist), three-fourths showed an immediate favorable response. The most valuable feature of the antagonist is that it overcomes the respiratory depression that may result from an overdose of opiates. Narcan has also proved useful for the diagnosis of opiate overdosage by observing the victim's response to the narcotic antagonist.

The general symptoms of methadone overdosage are the same as for heroin. The treatment used in emergency medicine is also the same as for narcotics in general. Narcan can counter respiratory depression caused by the opiate drugs, but it has a relatively short duration of action and must be given repeatedly if the patient remains unresponsive. Narcan must be used with extreme caution by a physician since it may cause an exaggerated withdrawal reaction with convulsions. Since an overdose of any opiate can cause death by respiratory depression, Narcan minimizes arrest of breathing by counteracting the depressant effects of the drug. A respiratory stimulant may be administered in conjunction with the narcotic antagonist. If the patient fails to respond to the injection of Narcan, other drugs become suspect. Definite withdrawal symptoms will be noted after an injection of the narcotic antagonist. Second and third injections of Narcan may be given in suspected cases of narcotic addiction when the patient does not respond to the first test. Lorfan is a drug that produces similar effects to those of Narcan, but is ten times more potent. Neither of these substances is effective against respiratory depression due to nonnarcotic drugs or other conditions.

It has often been found in medical studies that narcotics and other drugs may exaggerate the effects of each other. In other words, the effects of two or more drugs taken at the same time may be greater than would be expected by a mere process of addition. It appears to be well established that the use of a combination of drugs gives a greater chance for overdosage than from any single product. In 90 percent of the cases there was an association with the use of other drugs, including alcohol. Death may occur because of depression of the respiratory center of the brain.

Physicians conclude that being in a methadone program does not protect the addict from the dangers involved, either from the drug itself or from others that may aggravate respiratory depression. Alcohol appears to be the drug that is most often associated with an overdosage of methadone.

Narcotic Antagonists

Narcotic antagonists block the effects of opiate drugs and it has been assumed by some researchers that this influence will tend to encourage addicts to give up the use of narcotics.

The narcotic antagonist, *Naltrexone*, blocks the effects of opiates. Therefore, heroin, morphine sulfate, demerol or related compounds will not produce a "high." The value of Naltrexone lies in its capacity to neutralize or counteract the effects of opiates. However, a very potent narcotic can override the antagonist. The objective is to provide the addict with a temporary aid in overcoming reactional cravings.

About 80 to 90 percent of narcotic addicts who are released from treatment will eventually revert to the use of drugs again. Antagonistic products do not change this expectation in any manner. What the addicts tend to do is avoid the narcotic antagonist treatment rather than the narcotic drugs themselves.

Success in remaining free from addiction appears to depend on the personality of the individual rather than the treatment being followed. The antagonist approach requires personal responsibility and motivation. Participation at Narcotics Anonymous group meetings can be both influential and supportive. Like other 12 step programs, a drug free philosophy is encouraged. The addict needs to work these steps in all activities. Frontiers are borders, and in our development we meet them again and again. Some frontiers are very generous and exciting, while others are frightening and dangerous. Certainly this program is a frontier for the addict. Honesty, open mindedness, and willingness are "How" any addict begins the recovery process.

_____ QUOTATION _____

A frontier is never a place; it is a time and a way of life. Frontiers pass, but they endure in their people.

Hal Borland

Understanding AIDS

The Surgeon General of the United States, offers the following conclusions about AIDS.

1. AIDS is one of the most serious health problems that has ever faced the American public.

2. The AIDS virus slowly destroys the immune system of the body and makes it unable to fight other diseases. It is an opportunistic disease, so other pathogens are able to become established.

3. Sexual behavior, such as anal or oral intercourse is the leading cause of AIDS. Drug addicts who share infected needles or babies born to mothers with the disorder may develop AIDS.

4. The male gay population was the first group in the United States to suffer from AIDS.

5. AIDS has now joined other sexual diseases, such as chlamydia, gonorrhea, herpes and other sexually transmitted diseases as a serious threat to human health.

160

6. For most persons sex with one mutually faithful, and uninfected partner is the best protection against AIDS.

7. A person may be infected with AIDS without showing any signs of the disease. The only way to find out is to take a test for AIDS.

8. There is no present cure for AIDS.

9. The Public Health Service recommends counseling and testing for AIDS if a person: 1) has been infected with any sexually transmitted disease; 2) has shared the use of a needle with a drug addict; 3) is a male and has had sex with another man; or 4) has had sex with a bisexual male or a prostitute, male or female.

10. If you need more information, telephone your local health department, an AIDS "hotline" or call 1–800–342–AIDS.

If you have a positive test your outlook may be somewhat uncertain but it still may be possible that people with positive tests will stay healthy and will not get AIDS. But, you should take further precautions if you get a positive test. It's obviously important if you have a positive test to remember the safety of other people. Take real precautions to prevent the transmission of the virus to someone else through known means of contact.

When people get positive tests, they have to worry about the possibility of getting AIDS, but more seriously they have to look at a future that looks pretty cloudy. The fact is that most people who have AIDS will die of the disease.

A positive antibody reaction after taking the Elisa test, would reveal the presence of the HIV (virus). If you suspect exposure has occurred, keep in mind that the test is not accurate until approximately six months later. In other words, the potential AIDS victim will have months of worry prior to test verification, positive or negative. The virus gets transmitted in ways that are very intimate forms of contact. There are three basic ways:

1. The AIDS virus is most often spread by sexual contact between any two people if one of those people is infected. And that means a man can give it to another man, a man can give it to a woman, and it may even be possible for a woman to give it to another woman. The virus is also transmitted by blood. It is important to realize that the virus is not restricted to any specific kind of people.

2. Transmission by blood means three things. First, the virus can be transmitted by shared needles. Should the addict be using unsanitary materials, it is much more likely that some physical complaints will require treatment. Among 633 heterosexual intravenous drug users studied in San Francisco, 35 percent of daily cocaine injectors carried the AIDS virus as compared with 19 percent of daily heroin injectors. An unusually high incidence of hepatitis (liver infection), abscesses, hive-like reactions, respiratory and acute gastrointestinal distress or cramps are part of the high-dose methamphetamine syndrome.

161

Second, it can be transmitted by blood that is transfused for medical reasons. So be careful not to donate blood or organs where you could transmit infected blood to someone else by those routes. Fortunately, since the test has become available, blood has become safer. The risk of getting AIDS by blood transfusion is very low, about 1 case in 100,000.

The third way to get this virus is by accidents in medical health care. If a laboratory technician, a nurse, or a physician taking care of a patient with AIDS should suffer a needlestick injury, exposure has taken place.

3. The final way that the AIDS virus is spread from one person to another is by what is called perinatal transmission. That means that the virus can spread from an infected woman to her baby before birth. Women who get infected should not get pregnant.

If you think about those means of transmission, then you can figure out pretty easily what you have to worry about and what you don't. This virus is not transmitted by any form of casual contact. Most of the ordinary things you do with people aren't risky at all. It is certainly not a risk to sit in the same car, or next to each other in a movie, or to share the same dining room. The virus in not transmitted by air nor is it spread by coughing or sneezing. It also doesn't swim. Toilets, showers or swimming pools are not a risk.

On the other hand, there are clearly things that will transmit this virus. The most important one for most people is sexual contact. Sexual contact is a very effective way to spread this virus. If you had to design a system to carry this virus from one person to another, it would be hard to find a better way than sex.

There's some hierarchy of risk here and some sexual activities are more risky than others. One high-risk example is sexual activities that involve the anus. It is through anal intercourse with reception of male sperm inside the intestinal tract by either male or female, that spreads the fatal disease. Anal activity is the highest risk sexual activity. If you have anal sex without the protection of a condom, the act is even higher risk for the transmission of the virus. Vaginal sex between a man and a woman poses risk for the woman if she has unprotected contact with a man who is infected. There's some risk for the man if he has unprotected contact with a woman who is infected as well. Oral sex is harder to evaluate, although the Surgeon General identifies unprotected acts to be very risky. People worry a lot about other activities. How risky is it to kiss someone else? Well, it seems very clear now that the AIDS virus is not transmitted by saliva. So kissing that involves simply the exchange of saliva is probably not a risk at all.

162

Dr. Michael Ledermans article on the "Transmission of the Acquired Immunodeficiency Syndrome Through Heterosexual Activity," indicates that exposure to the AIDS virus has occurred among many prostitutes. It is likely that these men and women have engaged in anal sex activity with gay men suffering from the disease. It is uncertain as to how great the risk may be to either a heterosexual or bisexual male of acquiring AIDS from infected prostitutes. Other forms of transmission include sexual intercourse involving a male intra-venous drug addict and an unsuspecting female. A majority of AIDS infected drug users are self-injecting cocaine.

You have to make some choices that involve taking responsibility, being accountable to yourself and your sexual partner. Think enough of yourself and your sexual partners to take precautions: that you'll be consistent, that you'll think enough of yourself to not let anything get in the way of your health. It comes down to self-respect.

Much more difficult for many people is the issue of sexual activity. You need to make some important decisions about your sex life and how sexually active to be. There are a lot of options here.

First, you need to negotiate with sexual partners about having safer sex. Safer sex means not doing anything risky and taking precautions to prevent the transmission of any sexually transmitted disease. Second, you need to decide what you're going to do and what you are not going to do. Know your partners better, and for most people that means having fewer sexual contacts. Learn more about your partner and his or her health history and preferences before ending up in bed. Part of that means you have to be careful about using alcohol or drugs in the setting of sexual activity. Sometimes, if you've used a mind altering chemical, it can impair your judgment. You may end up doing things you wish you hadn't done. But if you think ahead of time, you have a better chance of safer sex. You have to learn how to put the condom on right. You have to be careful to use lubricants that are water based. You have to be careful that the condom stays on, that it stays intact, that it is taken off properly.

You need to understand that this could happen to you, but that you are in control of whether it does or not. And your control means precautions, condoms, negotiations, thinking ahead of time, and self-respect.

Summary

For narcotic addiction to occur, drugs must be introduced to a susceptible person. It is self-evident that if such persons could be prevented from having contact with, and continued access to, illicit narcotics, there would be very little addiction. Thus, measures taken to eliminate illicit drug traffic, are crucial preventive techniques. Designer drugs are a direct response to the increasingly high-tech, scientific orientation of our society. It is not a crime to be an addict, but it is a crime to possess or sell illicit drugs, and to steal.

The addict will lose self-esteem, family, the will to live and eventually the competence to function normally.

Most people tend to view intoxication by looking at alcohol, but unlike that drug, narcotics can leave the addict apparently clear-headed and steady, a paradox of opiates. There is no way to predict when an addiction will impair performance, particularly in its early stages.

There is no stereotypical impaired doctor or nurse. Most health professionals resort to the use of drugs because of pressure and problems that cannot be handled. Physicians in general abuse drugs more than the population at large. Pharmaceuticals are more readily available to doctors and they work under a peculiar kind of stress. But as tolerance increases, the all-consuming goal becomes the avoidance of withdrawal. A sharp distinction needs to be drawn between the average doctor's considerable technical knowledge of drugs and their effects, and the near-ignorance of the disease of addiction.

The extensive use of heroin in Viet Nam by American soldiers had parallel foundations. They were all out of control of their lives. Their basic life choices were not in their own hands. A feeling of powerlessness, of being unable to influence one's situation in a positive way, is as great a factor in addiction as fear.

A majority of AIDS infected drug users are self-injecting cocaine. Counseling and testing for AIDS is recommended if a person has shared the use of a needle with a drug addict or has been infected with any sexually transmitted disease, is a male and has had sex with another man, or has had sex with a bisexual male or a prostitute, male or female.

Self-Test

1. Identify the correct statement: (A) there is no stereotypical impaired doctor or nurse in terms of usage patterns; (B) the State Board of Registered Nurses may leave an impaired nurse on the job; (C) narcotics can leave the addict apparently clear-headed and steady; (D) addicts of any background will be overcome by their efforts to get ever-increasing amounts of the drug; (E) all of the foregoing.

2. The medical speciality which has the highest rate of addiction to prescription narcotics is: (A) surgeons; (B) internists; (C) anaesthesiologists; (D) Oncologists; (E) nurses.

3. An overdose of Methadone or any other narcotic should respond to an injection of: (A) Naltrexone; (B) Narcan; (C) Disulfiram; (D) Androstanedione; (E) SK-65.

4. An overdose of narcotics and/or alcohol can cause death by: (A) respiratory depression; (B) cardiac arrhythmia followed by asystole; (C) hyperthermia; (D) electrolyte imbalance; (E) seizure disorders.

164

5. When designer drugs like fentanyl first hit the streets: (A) most were legal; (B) chemists may have made as many as two dozen versions, releasing one at a time; (C) the skilled designer chemists manipulate the drug structure slightly to avoid governmental regulations; (D) the analogs of fentanyl may vary, making it from 100 to 6,000 times stronger than morphine; (E) all of the foregoing.

6. Cross-tolerance tends to develop among drugs in the same class. Identify the two drugs that will produce equivalent tolerance: (A) cocaine and methamphetamine; (B) Crystal Meth and Crack; (C) codeine and Darvon; (D) morphine and MDMA; (E) nicotine and alcohol.

7. The Vietnam experience makes clear the kind of pressures that may drive a person to become an addict. The most significant influence: (A) everpresent fear and discomfort; (B) a feeling of powerlessness, of being unable to influence one's situation in a positive way; (C) the absence of close relationships and the loss of meaningful work; (D) it's a disease in which a biological irregularity encoded in the genes has been fueled by misuse of a drug; (E) none of the foregoing.

8. Select the correct statement concerning AIDS: (A) For most persons sex with one mutually faithful, uninfected partner is the best protection; (B) a majority of AIDS infected drug users are self-injecting cocaine; (C) anal intercourse with reception of male sperm inside the intestinal tract by either male or female is the specific sex act that spreads the fatal disease; (D) the Elisa test is not acurate until approximately six months after exposure; (E) all of the foregoing.

ANSWERS: 1(E); 2(C); 3(B); 4(A); 5(E); 6(C); 7(D); 8(E)

Notes

1. "Reprinted from the PharmChem Newsletter c. 1988, PharmChem Laboratories, Inc., by permission."

Bibliography

1. Seymour, Richard, M.A. and David Smith, M.D., Darryl Inaba, Pharm. D., Mim Landry. *The New Drugs.* 164 pp. Hazelden Foundation, Center City, Minnesota. 1989.
2. Ludwig, Arnold, M.D. *The Alcoholic Mind.* 188 pp. Oxford University Press, New York, New York, 1988.
3. Gold, Mark S., M.D. *The Facts About Drugs and Alcohol.* 132 pp. Bantam Books, New York, New York, 1988.
4. Bateson, Mary Katherine and Richard Goldsby. *Thinking AIDS.* 153 pp. Addison-Wesley Publishing Co., Menlo Park, CA. 1988.
5. *Narcotics Anonymous.* 290 pp. World Service Office, Inc., 16155 Wyandoette Street, Van Nuys, CA 91406, 1984.

6. Rosenbaum, Marsha. *Women on Heroin.* pp. 196 Rutgers University Press, New Brunswick, New Jersey. 1981.
7. Byrd, Oliver E., M.D. and Thomas Byrd. *Medical Readings on Heroin.* 252 pp. Boyd and Fraser Publishing Co., San Francisco, CA. 1972.

E P I L O G U E

1. NOBODY EVER SAID THAT LIFE WAS GOING TO BE SAFE: Take some healthy risks. Human beings need variety in their life. Don't be afraid to change.

2. YOU WILL LEARN LESSONS: You are enrolled in a full-time informal school called life. Each day in this school you will have the opportunity to learn lessons. You may like the lessons or think them irrelevant and stupid.

3. THERE ARE NO MISTAKES ONLY LESSONS: Growth is a process of trial and error, experimentation. The "failed" experiments are as much a part of the process as the experiment that ultimately "works."

4. A LESSON IS REPEATED UNTIL LEARNED: A lesson will be presented to you in various forms until you have learned it. When you have learned it, you can go on to the next lesson.

5. LEARNING DOES NOT END: There is no part of life that does not contain its lessons. If you are alive, there are lessons to be learned. Your deeds today will be your memories tomorrow.

6. NO ONE CAN OUT-PERFORM YOUR OWN SELF-IMAGE. You cannot love or hate something about another person unless it reflects something you believe about yourself. Others are merely mirrors of you.

7. WHAT YOU MAKE OF YOUR LIFE IS UP TO YOU: You have all the tools and resources you need; what you do with them is up to you. The choice is yours.

8. YOUR ANSWERS LIE INSIDE YOU: When your "there" has become a "here", you will simply obtain another "there" that will look better than "here". The answers to life's questions lie inside you.

9. IF YOU TRAVEL FAR ENOUGH, YOU WILL EVENTUALLY MEET YOURSELF. You cannot run from yourself. You always bring your problems along.

10. WHAT YOU EARNESTLY GIVE IS FOREVER YOURS. It is better to give than to receive. The joy of giving, can never be taken away.